Cherished Teddies®

by ENESCO ®

FIFTH EDITION

Embrace the Earth

Secondary Market Price Guide
& Collector Handbook

Cherished Teddies®

EDITORIAL

Managing Editor:	Jeff Mahony
Associate Editors:	Melissa A. Bennett
	Gia C. Manalio
	Mike Micciulla
	Paula Stuckart
Assistant Editors:	Heather N. Carreiro
	Jennifer Renk
	Joan C. Wheal
Editorial Assistants:	Timothy R. Affleck
	Beth Hackett
	Christina M. Sette
	Steven Shinkaruk

PRODUCTION

Production Manager: Scott Sierakowski

ART

Creative Director:	Joe T. Nguyen
Assistant Art Director:	Lance Doyle
Senior Graphic Designers:	Marla B. Gladstone
	Susannah C. Judd
	David S. Maloney
	Carole Mattia-Slater
	David Ten Eyck
Graphic Designers:	Jennifer J. Bennett
	Sean-Ryan Dudley
	Kimberly Eastman
	Melani Gonzalez
	Jim MacLeod
	Jeremy Maendel
	Chery-Ann Poudrier

R&D

Product Development
Manager: Paul Rasid

ISBN   1-58598-149-4

CheckerBee PUBLISHING
306 Industrial Park Road
Middletown, CT 06457

CollectorsQuest.com

Table Of Contents

5   Introducing The Collector's Value Guide™
6   On The Teddies' Trail
12 Spotlight On Priscilla Hillman
16 Introducing The 2001 Cherished Teddies®
    Lineup
30 Collectors' Club News
31 Recent Retirements
32 Cherished Teddies® Top Ten
34 How To Use Your Collector's Value Guide™

35 FIGURINES

77 SERIES

77 Across The Seas	98 Friends Come In All
79 American Classics	Shapes And Sizes
80 Angels	99 Friends To The End
80 Antique Toys	100 Happily Ever After
81 Bear Business	101 Heart Strings
82 Beta Is For Bears	101 Holiday Dangling
84 Blossoms Of Friendship	102 John Deere
85 Bonnets And Bows	102 Just Between Friends
85 By The Sea, By The Sea	103 Let Heaven And Nature
86 Carousel	Sing
87 Carousel Birthstones	104 Lifetime Of Memories
89 Cherished Snowbears	104 Little Sparkles
89 Cherished Teddies	105 Love Letters From
And Friends	Teddie
91 Cherished Teddies	106 Monthly Friends To
Quilts	Cherish
91 Childhood Memories	
92 Circus	
94 Coca-Cola®	
94 Count On Me	
95 Days Of The Week	
96 Dicken's Village	
97 Down Strawberry Lane	
97 Follow The Rainbow	
98 The Four Seasons	

Table Of Contents

107 Nativity
109 Nursery Rhyme Series
110 Nutcracker Suite
111 Old Fashioned Country
     Christmas
111 Our Cherished Family
113 Our Cherished
     Neighbearhood
113 Our Cherished Wedding
114 Paint Your Own
114 Radio Flyer®
115 Santa Express
116 Santa Series
117 Santa's Workshop

118 School Days
119 Special Occasions
120 Springtime Angels
120 Sugar & Spice
121 Sweetheart Ball
122 T Is For Teddies
124 Teddie Triumphs
125 Teddies In Motion
126 Through The Years
127 Tumbling Teddies
128 Up In The Attic
129 We Bear Thanks
129 Winter Bear Festival

131 OTHER COLLECTIBLES

131 Bells
131 Bookends
131 Candleholders
132 Clocks
132 Eggs
133 Frames
137 Musicals

140 Ornaments
146 Plaques
150 Plates
152 Shadow Boxes
153 Tea Sets
153 Stocking Holders
154 Waterglobes

155 PLUSH

164 CHERISHED TEDDIES CLUBˢᴹ

170 Future Releases
172 Total Value Of My Collection
175 Teddies, Teddies Everywhere:
     Other Products
180 Spotlight On Glenn, The Designer
181 Secondary Market Overview
185 Variations
189 Insuring Your Collection
190 Numerical Index
197 Alphabetical Index

Introducing The Collector's Value Guide™

Welcome to the Collector's Value Guide to the Cherished Teddies® collection! Maybe you have seen these whimsical figurines at your neighborhood collectibles store or maybe you have gotten a piece as a gift.

Or perhaps you have been collecting for years, building your **Cherished Teddies** family into a whole forest full of these adorable teddies! Either way, this Value Guide has everything you need to know about **Cherished Teddies**. Here, you can find the latest information on collecting, selling and trading, as well as the value of your collection.

Also, you can read about the inspiring story of Priscilla Hillman, the talented artist whose creativity brought the **Cherished Teddies** to life. If you want to be a real **Cherished Teddies** insider, this is where you can find out how to join their official Collectors' Club. Regardless of whether you're a lifelong fan or a curious newcomer, you'll find all the latest info on your collection within these pages.

Look Inside To Find:

All the newest **Cherished Teddies** pieces for the year 2001

A look at the creations of Priscilla Hillman's son,

    designer Glenn Hillman

The history of the **Cherished Teddies** collection.

The best tips for trading your **Teddies** on the Internet

And much, much more!

On The Teddies' Trail

In 1992, the world of collectible figurines saw something new. It was a whole new line of adorable old-fashioned teddie bear figurines that sprang from the creative mind of a former oceanographer and illustrator named Priscilla Hillman. Those original 16 teddies would gradually multiply into a giant global family of bears, destined to take Enesco by storm and turn the collectibles world on its ear. But it took a woman's imagination combined with a sudden injury to bring those teddies to life.

Art Imitates Life

Just about everyone remembers drawing as a child, but Priscilla Hillman is one of those lucky folks who ended up doing it for a living. As a young girl, she and her twin sister, Greta, spent most of their time drawing together or exploring their aunt and uncle's attic. Both activities fed the young Priscilla's artistic nature, as well as her fondness for nostalgic antiques. Time spent puttering in the family garden affected her too, impressing upon her a great love of flowers and nature. Little did she know that all of these factors would later come together to bring the collectibles world a line the likes of which they had never seen.

Her fondness for nature led Priscilla to pursue a degree in botany at the University of Rhode Island, followed by a brief career with the U.S. Oceanographic Service. But her scientific endeavors gave way to her artistic impulses as she entered the world of children's books. With several illustration credits under her belt and even an unpublished series of her own, Hillman's future seemed assured. But then a sudden injury would lead her down yet another path.

Misfortune Becomes
A Fortunate Opportunity

While recuperating from a serious back injury in the late 1980s, Priscilla found herself with a copious amount of free time. To fill up those idle hours, she began to draw, but not with pen and paper as before. This time, she was using her own fertile imagination to fill her mind with drawings of teddie bears, adorable little critters who were destined to become the **Cherished Teddies** collection we all know and love!

Eugene Freedman

During the early 1990s, Eugene Freedman and Enesco were on the top of the collectibles world, basking in the popularity of the PRECIOUS MOMENTS® figurines. Searching for another line to continue his company's success, Gene Freedman learned about some charming, old-fashioned teddie bears and knew he had found what he was looking for. The paint on the original 16 bears was hardly dry when Priscilla found herself the proud recipient of a TOBY award from *Bearworld* magazine. A year later, that TOBY award was followed by the "Collectible of the Year" award from the National Association of Limited Edition Dealers.

In the years that followed, Priscilla showed collectors that she was so much more than a one-hit-wonder. Entire families of teddies filled store shelves – and disappeared just as quickly! It wasn't long before Priscilla's teddies took on distinct personalities. And there were bears for just about every occasion – from birthdays to Christmas to Easter to graduation.

The Expanding Family

With so many teddies to choose from, Priscilla began designing special series for her creations. So far, she has created nearly 60 separate series, incorporating such varied themes as *Dicken's Village, Nursery Rhymes* and *Teddies In Motion* into her designs. She has also embraced American popular culture by designing a Monopoly® figurine and even one with a Coca-Cola® theme. No matter which series they belong to, Priscilla's teddies will certainly never have to be lonely or bored!

The Birth Of A Teddie

When Priscilla has one of her artistic brainstorms, she sketches the teddie in color and the drawing is then sent to the manufacturers in Asia. A clay model is then meticulously crafted and used to make a rubber mold of the piece. That mold is then used to make the piece's "white body" (what the structure is called before its resin

attachments are added). Next, painting is slowly done by hand, with the master artists ensuring that the details are perfect. At the end of this process, each teddie's name and title are stamped on the bottom of the figurine. The item number and year mark are then handwritten on each piece.

Once the **Cherished Teddies** figurines have been made, they get to travel in style on their way to a new home. Protective material and a foam container keep each figurine safe inside its special box. A registration post card, a gift card and a Certificate of Adoption go with it as well, so you can welcome your teddie as part of the family!

You Mean There's More?

Although the **Cherished Teddies** figurines continue to be Priscilla's crowning achievement, she has expanded the designs to include other decorative items. The **Cherished Teddies** collection has turned up on just about everything you could possibly think of to make your home a prettier place. Candleholders, bookends, Easter eggs, frames and even collector plates are just some of the items that have poured from Priscilla's artistic soul.

But it doesn't end with resin creations. After all, what is a teddie bear good for if not for hugging? Priscilla has also included many bears of the "soft and cuddly" plush variety in her line, the perfect companion to snuggle with at night (or at any time)!

While the bears will always have a special place in Priscilla's heart, her creativity has branched out in a few other directions. Her love of animals has given rise to a whole zoo of other

collectible critters, including cats, mice and rabbits. Snowmen have also joined the fun, making for a crazy cast of characters to fill Priscilla's collectibles universe. And these creations are determined to be heard, as pieces such as Bryce actually make sounds.

The Family Business

Like any fine artist, Priscilla is always willing to take inspiration from what she sees every day – including her own family! Her husband, Norman, found himself and his fondness for fishing immortalized in one of his wife's figurines and Priscilla's son, Glenn, got a figurine too. "[I]t took some time for them to agree on what piece they wanted to 'be,'" said the artist, who even put herself into her work with the 1994 figurine, Priscilla Ann.

Artistic ability and imagination must run in the Hillman family. Glenn has gone into business with his mom and has helped to design a number of figurines – including the one that bears his own name!

A Friendly And Helping Paw

Despite her considerable talent and fame, Priscilla has never been one to hide from her fans or hoard her earnings. She's always been willing to share a smile with a collector, or let the fans know just who the woman is who designs their favorite line.

In the past year, special events have even given collectors a chance to break bread with their favorite artist – literally. The figurine, Diana, was available for purchase at special events in 2001, and the owners of pieces with a gold understamp won dinner with Priscilla at the 2001

Rosemont International Collectibles Exposition! What collector could pass that up?

Teddie bears and baseball are two of the last things anyone would expect to go together. But a piece inspired by Chicago Cubs star Ron Santo proves that they can go together like hot dogs and mustard!

Priscilla has frequently shown her compassionate side over the years. She has crafted a special piece, titled Booker & Fletcher, to raise money for St. Jude Children's Research Hospital®. Many of the kids at the hospital enjoy  using a Radio Flyer® wagon to get around, so they can surely emphasize with the wild and crazy bears in this piece! Seven percent of all profits from Booker & Fletcher are earmarked for the hospital, and, if they wish, purchasers of the piece can contribute an additional dollar.

It Keeps Growing And Growing . . .

With so many figurines to her credit and the promise of many more to come, it's interesting to wonder what Priscilla will do next. Her bears have celebrated Christmas, learned the Greek alphabet, explored outer space and even joined the United States military! Could they possibly be running out of things to do in their (infinite) spare time?

Of course not! For as long as Priscilla Hillman's imaginative inspiration continues, her creations – teddy bears and otherwise, from resin to plush to ceramic – will continue to entertain and delight collectors worldwide.

Spotlight On Priscilla Hillman

In 2000, a promotional event at collectibles stores nationwide gave collectors a chance to win dinner with Priscilla Hillman, the artistic lady whose **Cherished Teddies** creations have made the collectibles world just a bit cuter. As customers scrambled to try and meet their favorite creative mind, it made them wonder just what the talented Ms. Hillman is all about. How did a woman who once pursued a career in oceanography go from studying the vast ocean to crafting old-fashioned resin teddie bears? It may surprise you to learn that the process was really quite accidental.

Theater Of The Mind

After spending much of her early professional life with the U.S. Oceanographic Service, Priscilla finally got to show off her creative side with some time spent illustrating children's books.

Priscilla Hillman shows off the Steif bear which was mirrored after one of her very own designs.

She was even responsible for her own Doubleday series, starring Merry Mouse. It wasn't long after she finished her own as yet unpublished book, *Tumpy Rumple,* when her career was put on hold by a serious injury.

During the late 1980s, a serious back injury put Priscilla out of commission for a period of healing. With little to do, she began to use the creative mind that had always made children smile to imagine an adorable series of old-fashioned teddie bears. By the time she was out and about again, those teddies were ready to be given form as drawings, and later, as the **Cherished Teddies** bears beloved by so many collectors!

Priscilla Ann

Wells Of Inspiration

For inspiration, Priscilla used her own cheerful memories of childhood. As a young girl, she and her twin sister, Greta, would spend hours drawing, playing in their aunt and uncle's attic and puttering in the family garden. Priscilla's boundless imagination never forgot those special times, and those memories would prove to be her biggest asset.

Now, years later, the cute characters which inhabited her imagination have taken form as resin figurines, charming teddies with that characteristic antique look – right down to the patches on their paws! And it's no accident that so many of them have the look of teddie bears from days gone by.

"You never know when a new idea will come or what will inspire it."

"I have always loved nostalgic items," said Priscilla. "The Victorian era in particular." Priscilla was able to use her fondness for all things antique as one of her many sources of inspiration.

But her influences have never been limited to memories. Members of Priscilla's immediate family have been known to find themselves immortalized as **Cherished Teddies** characters, as pieces named for her husband, Norman, and her son, Glenn, have turned up on shelves everywhere. Even Priscilla herself has been spotted, as

Priscilla Hillman is always happy to sign pieces for her fans during collectibles shows.

the event exclusive, Priscilla Ann. And even the collectors provide inspiration as Priscilla sometimes uses names from the letters she receives for her teddies! No matter where she finds it, it seems that the talented Priscilla Hillman can put any kind of subject to work as a **Cherished Teddies** creation. "I look for inspiration around me every day," she said. "You never know when a new idea will come or what will inspire it."

Down Time

"I don't feel like a celebrity," said Priscilla. "Sometimes I have to be 'pinched' to realize that this is all real." For all her well-deserved fame among fans and collectors, Priscilla has never let it go to her head. She still lives in a modest New England colonial home (with a special room set aside for her teddies, of course) and still rises early every morning to dream up new activities and settings. When she's not designing her adorable bears, you can find her working in her English garden, eagerly awaiting the first birds of spring. Since her own family has inspired so many **Cherished Teddies** figurines, she loves to spend time with them as well. Who knows when she might decide to base another teddie on one of them?

It's a long way from playing in the garden with her sister, or puttering around the attic, but those girlhood memories have given Priscilla Hillman more than enough ideas to make all her artistic dreams – and those of all **Cherished Teddies** collectors – come true!

Priscilla Hillman and son, Glenn.

Spotlight On Priscilla Hillman

Introducing The 2001 Cherished Teddies® Lineup

This section spotlights the new **Cherished Teddies** pieces for 2001.

Figurines

 ABRAHAM ... *"YOUR FRIENDSHIP MEANS THE WORLD TO ME"* ... Abraham communes with his woodland friends and keeps an eye on the world!

"ABSENCE MAKES FRIENDSHIPS GROW STRONGER" ... When this brave teddie takes to the high seas, you can bet love and friendship will be felt in every port!

 ALMA AND AUSTIN ... *"LET ME CALL YOU SWEETHEART"* ... In this Cherished Retailer Exclusive, these sweeties know that the greatest happiness is found in each other's arms.

ANGELA ... *"THANKS FOR HELPING ME GET MY WINGS"* ... Angela can't wait to give her new snow-bear a set of wings and a halo all his own!

ASTRID ... *"IT'S NOT THE SIZE OF THE GIFT, BUT WHAT'S INSIDE THAT COUNTS"* ... Astrid makes sure that our hearts are in the right places this holiday season.

"AWAITING THE ARRIVAL" ... The cradle, rattle and bonnet are all set. But this teddie can't wait for that special little cub to come along!

 BEAR MERMAID ... This Adoption Center Event Exclusive piece is no doubt the most beautiful teddie in the sea.

BEATRICE ... *"HONEY, YOU'RE THE SWEETEST"* ... Disguising herself as a bee might not have been the best idea, but Beatrice got what she came for!

BOY WITH BOOKS AND APPLE . . . Could our little scholar be on his way to give his teacher a gift? Or is that apple for throwing purposes?

BOY WITH HORSE SHOE . . . You'll always have a little extra luck with this teddie watching over you.

BOY WITH SUITCASES . . . It's time to see the world, as our intrepid traveler takes off for new and fabulous adventures in faraway lands!

BOY WITH THANK YOU CARD . . . This teddie will always be grateful for your trusting friendship!

BRADLEY . . . *"FRIENDS ARE THE BEST CURE FOR THE WINTER BLUES"* . . . After playing around in the snow, Bradley's love will warm you up.

BRENNA . . . *"NOTHING MAKES LIFE MORE SPECIAL THAN BEING SURROUNDED BY FRIENDS"* . . . Brenna, the Winter Show Exclusive, and her friends know that with good friends around, you can do anything!

BRYCE . . . *"I SCORED A STRIKE WHEN I MET YOU"* . . . It looks like they forgot to tell Bryce that you're supposed to *let go* of the ball when you're bowling!

CARLA . . . *"CHOCOLATE IS A BEAR'S BEST FRIEND"* . . . Is there such a thing as too much chocolate? Maybe, but Carla certainly doesn't think so!

CARLTON . . . *"A TUMBLE IN THE SNOW BRINGS LOTS OF HO-HO-HO'S!"* . . . With his bell at the ready, Carlton will be rolling onto a lot of store shelves!

CAROLINE . . . *"LIKE THE STARS OF HEAVEN, I'LL LIGHT THE WAY"* . . . This angelic bear will always show all her friends the way to happiness!

"CIRCLE OF LOVE" . . . In this Syndicated Catalog Exclusive, this cute quartet of critters is a group that knows the meaning of true friendship.

CYNTHIA, ETHEL, NANETTE, LOLA, OPAL & JANEL . . . *"LOVE PASSES FROM GENERATION TO GENERATION"* . . . From the youngest to the oldest, this teddie family enjoys sharing love.

DANNY . . . *YOU'RE THE FINEST FRIEND IN THE FOREST* . . . Danny just carries that shotgun around for show. He's really a teddie bear at heart!

DAWN . . . *"YOU DON'T HAVE TO SEARCH FAR TO FIND YOUR RAINBOW"* . . . Dawn shows that something as beautiful as a rainbow may be just around the corner!

DELIA . . . *"YOU'RE THE BEARY BEST BABYSITTER"* . . . This special bear is always ready to watch over the neighbor's cubs when they need her.

DENNIS AND BARB . . . *I KNEW I WOULD FALL FOR YOU* . . . There's nothing quite like the autumn season, when some lucky teddie bears find that special someone! Will it be you?

DESTINY AND KAY . . . *"YOU'VE NEVER LOOKED MORE BEAUTIFUL THAN YOU DO TODAY"* . . . They say there's nothing more special than your daughter's wedding day!

DIANA ... *"I CHERISH YOUR BEAR HUGS"* ... Adorable teddies are made for hugging, and Diana, the Adoption Center Exclusive, knows it! This piece was named for Priscilla's favorite signature phrase.

DORIS ... *"I JUST CALLED TO SAY I LOVE YOU"* ... Get all the juiciest gossip, and a phone gift assortment from the chatty Doris.

DREW ... *"BEING SURROUNDED BY MY FAVORITE THINGS ALWAYS MAKES THINGS BETTER"* ... Drew isn't exactly a morning bear!

EDNA ... *"THE LEAVES OF CHANGE BRING BACK THE FONDEST MEMORIES"* ... This Homecoming Weekend Collector Figurine features leaves made of genuine lead crystals, which Edna is no doubt admiring.

ESTHER ... *"I'M SURROUNDED BY SPECIAL FRIENDS"* ... It's not hard to guess what holiday Esther is celebrating (hint: it sounds like her name!).

ETHAN ... *"AS LONG AS THE STAR SHINES, I SHALL FOLLOW IT"* ... When he first saw that shining star, Ethan knew what he had to do!

EVE ... *"EVERYONE NEEDS SOMEONE TO WATCH OVER THEM"* ... This cub will never be alone as long as a guardian angel like Eve watches from above!

FAY ... *"AN ANGEL'S TOUCH IS NEVER FAR AWAY"* ... True to the spirit of giving, Priscilla Hillman's profits from this angel bear (named for a close friend and collector) go to the American Cancer Society®.

COLLECTOR'S VALUE GUIDE™

Introducing The 2001 Cherished Teddies® Lineup

GIRL WITH STETHOSCOPE . . . This teddie won't need any instruments to hear your heart beat in time with her own!

 **"GREAT FRIENDSHIPS MAKE A SOLDIER STAND TALL"** . . . Even without a map, the way to your heart is easy for this soldier bear to find!

GUY . . . *"I COME BEARING GIFTS FOR EVERYONE!"* . . . Guy is so generous – he just can't help giving away so many presents!

 **"I JUST CALLED TO SAY I LOVE YOU"** . . . It's hard work being part of a Mother's Day Gift Set and now it's time for Mom to sit back and relax.

ICABOD . . . *"HAPPY HOLLOW-WEEN!"* . . . We know Icabod isn't exactly spooky, but humor him and look scared when he rings your doorbell!

 **JAN AND ELISE** . . . *"THIS IS THE START OF YOUR BRIGHT AND EXCITING FUTURE"* . . . This loving mother bear knows that her daughter will rise to any occasion!

JANICE . . . *"YOU SUIT ME PERFECTLY"* . . . Janice, a Regional Convention Event Exclusive, has been looking forward to this day at the beach for weeks!

 **KATHERINE** . . . *"YOU'RE THE BEST IN THE BUSINESS"* . . . This savvy businesswoman is ready to face whatever the day ahead may offer – after her coffee, of course!

"LIFE IS SMOOTH SAILING WITH YOU" . . . With a brave, seagoing bruin like this guarding the shore, you can bet your coastline will always be safe!

MIMI, DARCIE AND MISTY . . . **"THERE'S ALWAYS TIME FOR FRIENDS** . . . **AND A GOOD CUP OF TEA"** . . . Business should *never* interfere with tea (or honey) time!

PALMER AND CHARLENE . . . **"CLOWNING AROUND"** . . . These two decided to join the circus just for the fun of it, and now they're the star attraction!

PATTY AND PEGGY . . . **"SPENDING TIME WITH YOU IS PRICELESS"** . . . When two teddies get together to shop till they drop, there's just no stopping them!

PAUL REVERE . . . **"YOU CAN ALWAYS TRUST ME TO BE THERE"** . . . Paul is determined to bring **Cherished Teddies** bears everywhere the latest and greatest news!

PAULA . . . **"HELPING OTHERS IS THE BEST PART OF MY JOB"** . . . Count on Paula's nursing skills to make you feel better – whether you're sick or not!

"PRISCILLA AND CLARA" . . . This colorful piece reveals the delight to be had in a beautiful spring day that just begs to be spent in the garden.

ROBERTA . . . *"BEING YOUR FRIEND IS MY FAVORITE PASTIME"* . . . Tennis bums had better watch out when Roberta takes the court. She'll take them all on!

"THE SKY'S THE LIMIT" . . . You can count on hearing tales of exotic lands when this brave teddie comes in for a landing!

SONNY . . . *"GETTING READY FOR SANTA'S VISIT"* . . . This little guy from the Holiday Gift Set just can't wait for Santa to drop by.

SPARKY . . . *"YOUR CHEERFUL WAYS BRING BETTER DAYS"* . . . Being part beanbag has made Sparky's clowning job even easier!

SPRING BONNET FIGURINES . . . *"LOVE IS THE POETRY OF THE SOUL," "GIVE LIFE A HUG," "FRIENDS ARE THE SPICE OF LIFE"* . . . These lovely ladies will be hopping into your heart as Avon exclusives.

STEPHANIE AND MELANIE . . . *"TEA AND COOKIES WARM THE SOUL, BUT CLOSE FRIENDS WARM THE HEART"* . . . It's time for cookies, tea and a serious gab session!

TERRY . . . *"ALWAYS STAY ON TRACK ABOUT THE TRUE MEANING OF CHRISTMAS"* . . . There's nothing like giving (or getting) a brand new toy train to make a memorable Christmas!

TORI . . . *"FRIENDS ARE THE SWEETEST PART OF LIFE"* . . . "Tori" loves watermelon so much, and for a limited time, she is willing to share it with you when you make a **Cherished Teddies** purchase.

TROY . . . *"LIFE'S A BEACH!"* . . . It looks like Troy, a Regional Convention Event Exclusive, is ready to try his paw at underwater fishing.

WANDA . . . *"A SPRINKLING OF FAIRY DUST WILL MAKE YOU FEEL BETTER"* . . . With her bucket of coins in paw, Wanda makes kids happy to lose a tooth!

WENDALL . . . *"HAVE YOU BEEN NAUGHTY OR NICE?"* . . . It looks like Wendall is helping Santa with that all-important list this year! Are you on it?

"WHATEVER THE DISTANCE, A FRIEND STAYS WITH YOU" . . . This proud officer is looking for a few good bears to join him on the quest to be the cutest!

"WHEN I NEED A HUG, I RUN TO DAD!" . . . In this Father's Day piece, a little cub knows exactly where to go for a hug, or a little fatherly advice. Papa Bear always has plenty of both!

American Classics

JERALD AND MARY ANN . . . *"WHAT WOULD GAME NIGHT BE WITHOUT YOU?"* . . . When these two settle down for a game of Monopoly®, they know a little friendly competition won't get in the way of friendship.

Cherished Snowbears

DELIGHT . . . *"I WILL MELT YOUR HEART"* . . . Delight may be made of snow, but there's enough warmth, love and kindness inside all that snow for both of you!

ERIKA . . . *"REMEMBER THE PAST, CHERISH THE YEARS AHEAD"* . . . Even as she looks forward to feeding the birds in the spring, Erika is the perfect reminder that there is plenty to celebrate in the winter months, as well.

NORA . . . *"BRRRRRR"* . . . No matter how cold it is, Nora is determined to get her snowy friend home! Keep pulling that sled, Nora! You can do it!

URSULA & BERNHARD . . . *"IN THE WINTER, WE CAN BUILD A SNOWMAN"* . . . These two love cold weather, and they've waited all year to get out in the snow!

Quilts

"I'M A BEARY LUCKY GROOM" . . . That special day has come at long last, and the hero of our story can't wait to say "I do!"

"YOU HAVE TAUGHT ME WHAT IT MEANS TO BE A FRIEND" . . . There's nothing like a quilt to keep warm on a cold night. And the best friendships are just as cozy!

Childhood Memories

CALVIN . . . *"LIFE IS FILLED WITH UPS AND DOWNS"* . . . It looks like Calvin has got his yo-yo a little tangled up. But that's just life!

Coca-Cola®

DEWEY . . . *"ENJOY YOUR FRIENDS, THEY'RE THE REFRESHMENTS OF LIFE"* . . . This bear knows that nothing refreshes better after a long day than an icy glass of Coke® and a friend to share it with!

Days Of The Week

FRANCES ... *"FRIDAY'S CHILD IS LOVING AND GIVING"*. ... True to her generous nature, Frances loves to help out with the littlest cubs.

MONICA ... *"MONDAY'S CHILD IS FAIR OF FACE"* ... Any bear with a face as lovely as Monica's certainly can't help taking a glance in the mirror!

SANDRA ... *"SATURDAY'S CHILD WORKS HARD FOR A LIVING"* ... Not everyone is lucky enough to sleep late and relax on Saturday! That's Sandra's day to get things done!

SUNNY ... *"THE CHILD THAT IS BORN ON THE SABBATH DAY IS BONNY AND BLITHE AND GAY"* ... Sunny is ready to skip down the road to church, along with her beloved pet.

THELMA ... *"THURSDAY'S CHILD HAS FAR TO GO"* ... Where is Thelma going with all that luggage and a ticket? Wherever it is, she looks very prepared for her trip!

TIA ... *"TUESDAY'S CHILD IS FULL OF GRACE"* ... Have you ever seen such a graceful bear? Probably not, until now. Tia's natural ability is truly something to see!

WENDY ... *"WEDNESDAY'S CHILD IS FULL OF WOE"* ... There's no reason to be sad, so Wendy's own teddy bear is certainly lucky. Who else but Wendy would take such good care of him?

Friends To The End

GIRL STANDING . . . This teddie holds a friendship bracelet in its paw and it looks like it will fit you absolutely perfectly!

TWO GIRLS HUGGING . . . What are teddies – or best friends – made for? Hugging, of course!

TWO GIRLS STANDING . . . With their bracelet of friendship, these two form a chain of love that can never be broken!

Heart Strings

"BEST FRIENDS" . . . A little lady like this knows that friendship is the most valuable thing in the whole world!

"I LOVE YOU" . . . This teddie put all his creativity into making this simple card just for you!

"A KISS MAKES EVERYTHING BETTER" . . . A teddie knows that a kiss is better than anything else when you're down.

"U MAKE MY HEART SMILE" . . . This teddie's sweet sentiment will always ring true for lovers and friends!

"U R MY FAVORITE FRIEND" . . . Best friends are like teddies – they are both meant to be cherished!

"YOUR LOVE MAKES MY HEART SMILE" . . .
Your affection can make this teddie feel all the
better, no matter what!

John Deere®

CHUCK . . . "YOU'VE ALWAYS BEEN A DEERE
FRIEND" . . . After spending so many years living on
honey, Chuck decided it was time to go into the
farming business!

Let Heaven And Nature Sing

REBECCA . . . "LET HEAVEN AND NATURE SING" . . .
Rebecca has been known to sing the praises of her two
bunny companions.

Lifetime Of Memories

BILLIE . . . "A BUNDLE OF JOY FROM HEAVEN
ABOVE" . . . A special mama and papa bear will be
overjoyed to see Billie float down from the sky!

"OUR JOURNEY HAS JUST BEGUN" . . . The sky's the
limit as these joyous bears tie the knot and their exciting foray into the world of marriage begins.

Paint Your Own

TRINA . . . "MY MEMORIES OF YOU ARE KEPT IN MY
HEART" . . . What color do you think Trina's bonnet and
pillow should be? You get to decide!

Radio Flyer®

BOOKER AND FLETCHER . . . "TOGETHER, WHEREVER
WE GO" . . . These two wild and crazy bears are off to
see the world together.

VERNON AND EVA . . . *"WHEREVER LIFE TAKES YOU, I WON'T BE FAR BEHIND"* . . . Pulling that wagon can't be easy, but their friendship is worth the work!

Springtime Angels

WILLOW . . . *"CHERISHED YOUR SPIRIT"* . . . Anticipated for a year, this special bear has finally made her debut!

Teddies In Motion

ANDRE . . . *"THE FINISH LINE IS ONLY A LAP AWAY"* . . . Andre is all set to tear up the tracks and take the checkered flag. Let's hope he has a great pit crew!

BERT . . . *"I'M BUSY AS A BEE EVERY DAY OF THE WEEK"* . . . Like any bear, Bert loves his honey, and stops at nothing to get it home on time!

HOWARD . . . *"A-FARMING WE WILL GO"* . . . Howard has finished loading his truck with hay. Do you think he's noticed his hitchhikers yet?

WARREN . . . *"THERE IS NO LIMIT TO HOW FAR YOU CAN GO"* . . . Warren is ready to zoom up into the bluest skies and soar above the whitest clouds!

Other Collectibles

CANDLEHOLDERS . . . The "Three Bears" make an appearance this year as candleholders.

CLOCKS . . . Whether it's time for tea, or time to face a deadline, these clocks will remind you not to take things too seriously!

FRAMES ... When the leaves start to turn and the kids go back to school, why not display their pictures in some of these charming fall-themed frames, including the all-new *Friends To The End* frames.

MUSICALS ... Do you remember? The teddies honor those memories of your first time on a carousel with two new musicals. "Snowman With Scarf," has also joined the line.

ORNAMENTS ... Adorable bears like this would never dream of hibernating the winter away. They'd rather brighten your home by hanging from your Christmas tree's highest branches!

PLAQUES ... Any of these wonderful new plaques would be an excellent addition to any home. But don't get them too close to each other. They've been known to fight over that stuffed elephant!

PLUSH ... With a plush bear for every season, it won't be easy to decide which is your favorite! There are teddies for all major sports, seasons and joyous aromas.

SHADOW BOXES ... Whether your favorite season is autumn, spring, summer or fall, these shadow boxes will remind you of the cherished seasons all year round.

WATERGLOBES ... What better place for a teddie mermaid than in this fantastic waterglobe, available only through Adoption Centers and for a limited amount of time?

Collectors' Club News

The folks at Enesco can "bearly" wait to sign you up for *The Cherished Teddies Club*SM. When you join the club, you become one of almost 200,000 other "membears" who know that membearship in this exclusive Club carries all sorts of benefits.

For only a $20 membearship fee, you will receive all sorts of goodies like a subscription to *The Town Tattler*SM (the Club's official quarterly newsletter), a lapel pin, a full-color catalog and access to the exclusive Club website. Best of all, you'll get the 2001 Membearship Figurine, T. James Bear, the International Bear of Mystery. With his mysterious overcoat, hat and briefcase there's no telling where he'll show up – except in your mailbox!

This year, the drama of the popular soap opera, "A Bear's Life," continues "On Location" with four exclusive Membears' Only Figurines available for purchase. Maxine D'Face is all set to apply her make-up magic, while the soft-hearted bodyguard, Giacomo 'Jake' Bearcino, is ready to protect them all from danger.

They'll be certain to meet country singing sensation Deena Wilde as she tours Europe on her motorcycle with Angelo riding along in the sidecar. He comes free to you with the purchase of the other three figurines. And for those of you already in the club, remember, the early bird catches the 2001 Early Renewal Figurine, the "Mystery Bear." There's no mystery involved in becoming a member of *The Cherished Teddies Club*SM. Just contact:

The Cherished Teddies Club
P.O. Box 689
Itasca, IL 60143-0689
1-877-4YOURCLUB
www.enescoclubs.com

Recent Retirements

Several **Cherished Teddies** figurines have recently gone into permanent hibernation or "retirement," marking the end of their production. This section lists the **Cherished Teddies** pieces which have recently been retired, along with each piece's issue year and item number. Additionally, several Limited Editions have "closed" and many other collectibles have been taken out of production.

Retired in 2000!

Figurines

❑ Brooke . . . . (1998, #302686)
❑ Carol . . . . (1998, #352969)
❑ Cecilia . . . . (2000, #679089)
❑ Darren . . . . (2000, #784974)
❑ Erica . . . . (1996, #176028)
❑ Jean . . . . (1997, #269859)
❑ Joann . . . . (1997, #269840)
❑ Jordan . . . . (1997, #269832)
❑ Mary . . . . (1993, #912840)
❑ Val . . . . (2000, #738638)

Blossoms Of Friendship

❑ Dahlia . . . . (1997, #202932)
❑ Iris . . . . (1997, #202908)
❑ Lily . . . . (1998, #202959)
❑ Rose . . . . (1997, #202886)
❑ Susan . . . . (1997, #202894)

By The Sea, By The Sea

❑ Gregg . . . . (1997, #203505)
❑ Jerry . . . . (1997, #203475)
❑ Jim and Joey . . . . . . (1997, #203513)
❑ Judy . . . . (1997, #203491)
❑ Sandy . . . . (1997, #203467)

Carousel

❑ Bill . . . . (1999, #505552)
❑ Cody . . . . (1999, #505498)
❑ Gina . . . . (1999, #502898)
❑ Jason . . . . (1999, #506214)
❑ Jenelle . . . . (1999, #505579)
❑ Virginia . . . . (1999, #506206)

Circus

❑ Bruno . . . . (1996, #103713)
❑ Circus Elephant With
   Bear . . . . (1996, #103977)
❑ Circus Gift Set . . . . . (1996, #104256)
❑ Circus Lion . . . . (1997, #203548)

Circus, cont.

❑ Circus Seal With Ball . (1996, #137596)
❑ Claudia . . . . (1996, #103721)
❑ Dudley . . . . (1997, #103748)
❑ Logan . . . . (1997, #103756)
❑ Shelby . . . . (1997, #203572)
❑ Tonya . . . . (1997, #103942)
❑ Wally . . . . (1996, #103934)

Down Strawberry Lane

❑ Ella . . . . (1996, #156329)
❑ Jenna . . . . (1996, #156337)
❑ Matthew . . . . (1996, #156299)
❑ Tara . . . . (1996, #156310)
❑ Thelma . . . . (1996, #156302)

Happily Ever After

❑ Brett . . . . (1998, #302457)

Sugar & Spice

❑ Missy, Cookie & Riley (1998, #352586)
❑ Pamela and Grayson . . (1998, #352616)
❑ Sharon . . . . (1998, #352594)
❑ Wayne . . . . (1998, #352608)

Winter Bear Festival

❑ Adam . . . . (1997, #269751)
❑ Candace . . . . (1997, #269778)
❑ James . . . . (1997, #269786)
❑ Lindsey and Lyndon . . (1997, #141178)
❑ Mitch . . . . (1997, #269735)
❑ Spencer . . . . (1997, #269743)

Cherished Teddies® Top Ten

This section highlights the ten most valuable **Cherished Teddies** figurines as determined by their values on the secondary market.

Daisy (#910651)
Issued 1993 – Suspended 1995 – Retired 1996
Original Price: $15
Secondary Market Value: **Letter – $825**

Chelsea (#910694)
Issued 1993 – Suspended 1995 – Retired 1995
Original Price: $15
Secondary Market Value: **Letter – $295**

"Holding On To Someone Special" (#916285)
Issued 1993 – Closed 1993
Original Price: $20
Secondary Market Value: **No Mark – $245**

Alice (Dated 1993, #912875)
Issued 1993 – Closed 1993
Original Price: $17.50
Secondary Market Value: **3-mark – $240**

Priscilla Ann (#CRT025)
Issued 1994 – Closed 1995
Original Price: $25
Secondary Market Value: **4-mark – $230**

Tasha (International Exclusive, #156353F)
Issued 1996 – Closed 1996
Original Price: $55
Secondary Market Value: **6-Mark – $225**

Charity (#910678)
Issued 1993 – Suspended 1994 – Retired 1996
Original Price: $20
Secondary Market Value: **Letter – $200**

Teddy and Roosevelt (#624918)
Issued 1993 – Closed 1993
Original Price: $20
Secondary Market Value: **3-Mark – $198**

Beth And Blossom (#950564)
Variation: with butterfly
Issued 1992 – Retired 1997
Original Price: $50
Secondary Market Value: **Letter – $195**

Bessie (#916404)
Issued 1994 – Suspended 1995
Original Price: $15
Secondary Market Value: **3-Mark – $180**

How To Use Your Collector's Value Guide™

1. Locate your piece in the Value Guide. The pieces are listed alphabetically with general figurines listed first, followed by figurine series (listed alphabetically by series name). Other **Cherished Teddies** collectibles (frames, ornaments, plates, etc.) come next and the section concludes with plush and Club exclusives. Seasonal pieces are listed in the general figurines section and are marked with symbols denoting the appropriate theme. Easy-to-use alphabetical and numerical indexes can be found in the back of the book.

Abigail
'Inside We're All The Same'
Issued: 1993 • Suspended: 1995
Original Price: $16
Value by Year Mark:
LETTER –$110 3–$63 4–$54

2. Look at the handwritten registration number on the bottom of your piece. The first number or letter of this registration number is considered the year mark.

3. Find the value which corresponds with the year mark on the bottom of your piece (some year marks may not be listed). For pieces produced without year marks or with undetermined year marks, only one value is listed. Pieces for which a secondary market value is not established are listed with values as "N/E." Pieces that were suspended, but were returned to production are noted with a triangle (Δ).

Figurines

	Price Paid	Value
1.		
2.	$16	$54
3.		
4.		
5.		
6.		
7.		
	$16	$54
	Totals	

4. Record the original price that you paid and the current value of the piece in the boxes at the bottom of the page.

5. Transfer the totals from each page to the "Total Value Of My Collection" worksheets on pages 172-174. Add all of the totals together to determine the overall value of your collection. Use a pencil so you can change the totals as your collection grows!

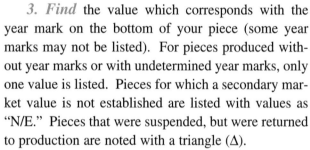

♥	Valentine's Day	🎃	Halloween
♣	St. Patrick's Day	🦃	Thanksgiving
❀	Spring/Easter	▲	Winter/Christmas

Figurines

Each year has brought more and more Cherished Teddies into the spotlight, and 2001 was no exception. There are even five figurines in honor of the men and women who serve in the United States Armed Forces! Never let it be said that the brave Cherished Teddies ever ignored their country!

1 #302708

"25 Years To Treasure Together"
Issued: 1998 • Current
Original Price: $30
Value by Year Mark: 7-$33 8-$30
9-$30 I-$30 II-$30

2 #900362

Abigail
"Inside We're All The Same"
Issued: 1993 • Suspended: 1995
Original Price: $16
Value by Year Mark:
LETTER-$110 3-$63 4-$54

3 #706876

New

Abraham (LE-10,000)
"Your Friendship Means The World To Me"
Issued: 2001 • Current
Original Price: $40
Value by Year Mark: I-$40 II-$40
Variation: International Exclusive, LE-10,000, #706876I
Value: N/E

4 #706957

New

"Absence Makes Friendships Grow Stronger"
Issued: 2001 • Current
Original Price: $17.50
Value by Year Mark:
I-$17.50 II-$17.50

5 #798835

Adelaide (Avon Exclusive)
Issued: 2000 • Closed: 2000
Original Price: $9.99
Value by Year Mark: I-N/E

6 #726702

Agatha (Abbey Press Early Release)
Issued: 2000 • Closed: 2000
Original Price: $14.95
Value by Year Mark: 9-$36 I-$20

7 #103594

"Aiming For Your Heart"
Issued: 1995 • Suspended: 1995
Original Price: $25
Value by Year Mark: 4-$40

8 #368156

Alex (1999 Event Exclusive)
"Cherish The Little Things"
Issued: 1999 • Closed: 1999
Original Price: $17.50
Value by Year Mark: 9-$62

Figurines

	Price Paid	Value
1.		
2.		
3.		
4.		
5.		
6.		
7.		
8.		

Totals

Figurines

1 #903620

Alice (9")
"Cozy Warm Wishes Coming Your Way"
Issued: 1993 • Suspended: 1995
Original Price: $100
Value by Year Mark:
3–$188 4–$155

2 #912875

Alice (Dated 1993)
"Cozy Warm Wishes Coming Your Way"
Issued: 1993 • Closed: 1993
Original Price: $17.50
Value by Year Mark: 3–$240

3 #127981

Allison & Alexandria
"Two Friends Mean Twice The Love"
Issued: 1995 • Retired: 1999
Original Price: $25
Value by Year Mark: 4–$55 5–$47
6–$40 7–$35 8–$30 9–$30

4 #789577
New

Alma And Austin (Cherished Retailer Exclusive, LE-2001)
"Let Me Call You Sweetheart"
Issued: 2001 • To Be Closed: 2001
Original Price: $40
Value by Year Mark: I–$40 II–$40

5 #533866

Alyssa
"You Warm My Soul"
Issued: 1999 • Current
Original Price: $15
Value by Year Mark:
8–$20 9–$15 I–$15 II–$15

6 #141186

Amanda (Dated 1995)
"Here's Some Cheer To Last The Year"
Issued: 1995 • Closed: 1995
Original Price: $17.50
Value by Year Mark: 5–$42

Figurines

	Price Paid	Value
1.		
2.		
3.		
4.		
5.		
6.		
7.		
8.		
9.		
10.		
Totals		

7 #910732

Amy
"Hearts Quilted With Love"
Issued: 1993 • Retired: 1999
Original Price: $13.50
Value by Year Mark:
LETTER–$66 3–$50 4–$40 5–$35
6–$33 7–$23 8–$18 9–$18
Variation: with lavender bow
Value: $65

8 #176265

Andy
"You Have A Special Place In My Heart"
Issued: 1996 • Retired: 1998
Original Price: $18.50
Value by Year Mark:
6–$36 7–$27 8–$23

9 #706809
New

Angela
"Thanks For Helping Me Get My Wings"
Issued: 2001 • Current
Original Price: $50
Value by Year Mark: I–$50 II–$50

10 #477915

Anita (1999 Catalog Exclusive)
"You're A Tulip To Treasure"
Issued: 1999 • Closed: 1999
Original Price: $20
Value by Year Mark: 9–$35

Figurines

1 #950459

Anna
"Hooray For You"
Issued: 1992 • Retired: 1997
Original Price: $22.50
Value by Year Mark:
LETTER–$80 **3**–$63 **4**–$47
5–$40 **6**–$37 **7**–$33

2 #534234

Anne
*"So Glad You're Here To
Keep Me Warm"*
Issued: 1999 • Current
Original Price: $10
Value by Year Mark:
8–$12 **9**–$10 **I**–$10 **II**–$10

3 #205354

Annie, Brittany, Colby, Danny and Ernie (5th Anniversary Piece, LE-1997)
*"Strike Up The Band And Give
Five Cherished Years A Hand"*
Issued: 1997 • Closed: 1997
Original Price: $75
Value by Year Mark: **7**–$78

4 #476978

"Anxiously Awaiting The Arrival"
Issued: 1999 • Current
Original Price: $15
Value by Year Mark:
8–$18 **9**–$15 **I**–$15 **II**–$15

5 #706698

Ariel (Dated 2000)
*"Everyone Needs A Little Help
Learning To Fly"*
Issued: 2000 • Closed: 2000
Original Price: $17.50
Value by Year Mark: **I**–$25

6 #476161

Arnold
"You Putt Me In A Great Mood"
Issued: 1999 • Current
Original Price: $17.50
Value by Year Mark:
8–$23 **9**–$17.50 **I**–$17.50 **II**–$17.50

7 #864218

New

Astrid
*"It's Not The Size Of The Gift,
But What's Inside That Counts!"*
Issued: 2001• Current
Original Price: $30
Value by Year Mark: **I**–$30 **II**–$30

8 #546526

Ava (1999 Avon Exclusive)
*"You Make Me Feel
Beautiful Inside"*
Issued: 1999 • Closed: 1999
Original Price: $19.99
Value by Year Mark: **8**–$35 **9**–$30

9 #663883A

Avon Millennium Exclusive (Avon Exclusive)
Issued: 2000 • Closed: 2000
Original Price: $9.99
Value by Year Mark: **9**–$15 **I**–$15

10 #743801

New

"Awaiting The Arrival"
Issued: 2001 • Current
Original Price: $20
Value by Year Mark: **I**–$20 **II**–$20

Figurines

	Price Paid	Value
1.	22.50	47⁰⁰
2.		
3.		
4.		
5.		
6.		
7.		
8.		
9.		
10.		
Totals		

Figurines

1 #203874

Baby With Diaper Shelf Sitter
Issued: 1997
Out Of Production: 2000
Original Price: $30
Value by Year Mark:
7–$35 8–$32 9–$32 I–$32

2 #270016

Barry
"I'm Batty Over You"
Issued: 1997 • Current
Original Price: $17.50
Value by Year Mark: 7–$28 8–$23
9–$17.50 I–$17.50 II–$17.50

3 #103586

"Be My Bow"
Issued: 1995 • Suspended: 1995
Original Price: $15
Value by Year Mark: 4–$40

4 #141348

Bea
"Bee My Friend"
Issued: 1995 • Retired: 1998
Original Price: $15
Value by Year Mark:
5–$29 6–$22 7–$20 8–$18

5 #865087

New

Bear Mermaid (2001 Adoption Center Event Exclusive)
Issued: 2001 • Current
Original Price: $15
Value by Year Mark: I–$15 II–$15

6 #786837

New

Beatrice
"Honey, You're The Sweetest"
Issued: 2001 • Current
Original Price: $20
Value by Year Mark: I–$20 II–$20

Figurines

	Price Paid	Value
1.		
2.		
3.		
4.		
5.		
6.		
7.		
8.		
9.		
10.		
Totals		

7 #916331

Becky
"Springtime Happiness"
Issued: 1994 • Suspended: 1995
Original Price: $20
Value by Year Mark: 3–$60 4–$50

8 #368237

Benjamin (U.K. Frequent Buyer Program, Level 3)
"Togetherness Is One Of The Bear Necessities"
Issued: 1999 • Closed: 1999
Original Price: N/A
Value by Year Mark: 9–$90

9 #950548

Benji
"Life Is Sweet, Enjoy"
Issued: 1992
Suspended: 1995 • Retired: 1995
Original Price: $13.50
Value by Year Mark:
LETTER–$65 3–$50 4–$42

10 #163457

Bertie (International Exclusive)
"Friends Forever Near Or Far"
Issued: 1995 • Current
Original Price: 17.50
Value by Year Mark: 5–$50 6–$40
7–$33 8–N/E 9–N/E I–N/E II–N/E

1   #916404

Bessie
"Some Bunny Loves You"
Issued: 1994 • Suspended: 1995
Original Price: $15
Value by Year Mark:
3–$180 4–$160

2   #127949

"The Best Is Yet To Come"
Issued: 1995 • Current
Original Price: $13.50
Value by Year Mark: 4–$33 5–$27
6–$20 7–$17 8–$15 9–$13.50
I–$13.50 II–$13.50

3   #127957

"The Best Is Yet To Come"
Issued: 1995 • Current
Original Price: $12.50
Value by Year Mark: 4–$28 5–$24
6–$17 7–$15 8–$15 9–$13.50
I–$13.50 II–$12.50

4   #950637

Beth
"Bear Hugs"
Issued: 1992
Suspended: 1995 • Retired: 1995
Original Price: $17.50
Value by Year Mark:
LETTER–$78 3–$60 4–$52

5   #950807

Beth
"Happy Holidays, Deer Friend"
Issued: 1992 • Suspended: 1995
Original Price: $22.50
Value by Year Mark: LETTER–$80
3–$62 4–$56 5–$43

6   #950564

Beth And Blossom
"Friends Are Never Far Apart"
Issued: 1992 • Retired: 1997
Original Price: $50
Value by Year Mark:
3–$85 4–$75 5–$70 6–$67
Variation: with butterfly
Value by Year Mark:
LETTER–$195 3–$162

7   #624896

Betsey
"The First Step To Love"
Issued: 1994 • Retired: 1999
Original Price: $12.50
Value by Year Mark: 3–$36 4–$32
5–$24 6–$19 7–$15 8–$14 9–$14

8   #533637

**Bette (1999 Adoption
Center Event Exclusive)**
"You Are The Star Of The Show"
Issued: 1999 • Closed: 1999
Original Price: $20
Value by Year Mark: 9–$32

9   #626066

Betty
"Bubblin' Over With Love"
Issued: 1994 • Current
Original Price: $18.50
Value by Year Mark: 3–$50 4–$41
5–$36 6–$24 7–$18.50 8–$18.50
9–$18.50 I–$18.50 II–$18.50

10   #533297

Bianca
"Sweet Dreams My Little One"
Issued: 1999 • Current
Original Price: $15
Value by Year Mark:
8–$17 9–$15 I–$15 II–$15

Figurines

	Price Paid	Value
1.		
2.		
3.		
4.		
5.		
6.		
7.		
8.		
9.		
10.		
Totals		

1 #624896

Billy
"Everyone Needs A Cuddle"
Issued: 1994 • Retired: 1999
Original Price: $12.50
Value by Year Mark: **3**–$42 **4**–$34
5–$25 **6**–$22 **7**–$18 **8**–$15 **9**–$15
Variation: spelled "Billie"
Value: $55

2 #624896

Bobbie
"A Little Friendship To Share"
Issued: 1994 • Retired: 1999
Original Price: $12.50
Value by Year Mark: **3**–$45 **4**–$32
5–$27 **6**–$21 **7**–$17 **8**–$15 **9**–$15

3 #706868

**Bobby
(International Exclusive)**
*"A Good Friendship Is Always
Worth Protecting"*
Issued: 2000 • Current
Original Price: $15
Value by Year Mark:
9–$50 **I**–$40 **II**–N/E

4 #466301

Bonnie And Harold
"Ring In The Holidays With Me"
Issued: 1998 • Current
Original Price: $25
Value by Year Mark:
8–$39 **9**–$27 **I**–$25 **II**–$25

5 #869082

Boy And Girl Cupid
"Heart To Heart"
Issued: 1995 • Suspended: 1995
Original Price: $18.50
Value by Year Mark: **4**–$44

6 #869082

Boy And Girl Cupid
"My Love"
Issued: 1995 • Suspended: 1995
Original Price: $18.50
Value by Year Mark: **4**–$44

7 #869074

Boy Cupid
"From My Heart"
Issued: 1995 • Suspended: 1995
Original Price: $13.50
Value by Year Mark: **4**–$38

8 #869074

Boy Cupid
"Sealed With Love"
Issued: 1995 • Suspended: 1995
Original Price: $13.50
Value by Year Mark: **4**–$40

9 #833428
New

**Boy With Books
And Apple**
Issued: 2001 • Current
Original Price: $10
Value: $10

10 #833312
New

Boy With Horse Shoe
Issued: 2001 • Current
Original Price: $10
Value: $10

Figurines

	Price Paid	Value
1.		
2.		
3.		
4.		
5.		
6.		
7.		
8.		
9.		
10.		
Totals		

Figurines

1 #833436
New

Boy With Suitcases
Issued: 2001 • Current
Original Price: $10
Value: $10

2 #833304
New

Boy With Thank You Card
Issued: 2001 • Current
Original Price: $10
Value: $10

3 #706833
New

Bradley (Limited Edition)
*"Friends Are The Best Cure
For The Winter Blues"*
Issued: 2001 • Current
Value by Year Mark: I–$15 II–$15

4 #354252

Brandon
"Friendship Is My Goal"
Issued: 1998 • Current
Original Price: $20
Value by Year Mark:
8–$25 9–$20 I–$20 II–$20

5 #617180

Breanna
"Pumpkin Patch Pals"
Issued: 1994 • Retired: 1998
Original Price: $15
Value by Year Mark:
4–$48 5–$38 6–$29 7–$23 8–$18

6 #912816

Brenda
*"How I Love Being
Friends With You"*
Issued: 1993
Suspended: 1995 • Retired: 1995
Original Price: $15
Value by Year Mark:
3–$76 4–$52 5–$45

7 #864315
New

**Brenna (Winter 2001
Show Exclusive)**
*"Nothing Makes Life More
Special Than Being Surrounded
By Friends"*
Issued: 2001 • Current
Original Price: $45
Value by Year Mark: I–$45 II–$45

8 #302686

Brooke
"Arriving With Love And Care"
Issued: 1998 • Retired: 2000
Original Price: $25
Value by Year Mark:
7–$33 8–$29 9–$27

9 #731870
New

Bryce
"I Scored A Strike When I Met You"
Issued: 2001 • Current
Original Price: $22.50
Value by Year Mark:
I–$22.50 II–$22.50

10 #912816

Buckey
*"How I Love Being
Friends With You"*
Issued: 1993
Suspended: 1995 • Retired: 1995
Original Price: $15
Value by Year Mark:
3–$68 4–$52 5–$45

Figurines		
	Price Paid	Value
1.		
2.		
3.		
4.		
5.		
6.		
7.		
8.		
9.		
10.		
Totals		

Figurines

1 #103802

Bunny
"Just In Time For Spring"
Issued: 1995 • Retired: 1998 ∆
Original Price: $13.50
Value by Year Mark:
4–$35 5–$28 6–$23 7–$17 8–$15

2 #156388

Butch
"Can I Be Your Football Hero?"
Issued: 1996 • Retired: 1999
Original Price: $15
Value by Year Mark:
5–$30 6–$24 7–$20 8–$17 9–$17

3 #508659

Cameron
(Canadian Exclusive)
"Our Friendship Is Building With Each New Adventure"
Issued: 1999 • Current
Original Price: N/A
Value by Year Mark:
9–$48 I–$35 II–N/E

4 #950424

Camille
"I'd Be Lost Without You"
Issued: 1992 • Retired: 1996
Original Price: $20
Value by Year Mark: *LETTER*–$70
3–$51 4–$39 5–$32 6–$29

5 #215856

"Can't Bear To See You Under The Weather"
Issued: 1997 • Current
Original Price: $15
Value by Year Mark:
7–$30 8–$22 9–$15 I–$15 II–$15

6 #706620

New

Carla
(Limited Edition)
"Chocolate Is A Bear's Best Friend"
Issued: 2001 • Current
Original Price: $20
Value by Year Mark: I–$20 II–$20

7 #533874

Carlin & Janay
"When I Count My Blessings, I Count You Twice"
Issued: 1999 • Current
Original Price: $25
Value by Year Mark:
8–$27 9–$25 I–$25 II–$25

8 #873438

New

Carlton
"A Tumble In The Snow Brings Lots Of Ho-Ho-Ho's!"
Issued: 2001 • Current
Original Price: $15
Value by Year Mark: I–$15 II–$15

9 #352969

Carol
"Angels Snow How To Fly"
Issued: 1998 • Retired: 2000
Original Price: $17.50
Value by Year Mark:
8–$26 9–$21 I–$19

10 #864277

New

Caroline
"Like The Stars Of Heaven, I'll Light The Way"
Issued: 2001 • Current
Original Price: $22.50
Value by Year Mark:
I–$22.50 II–$22.50

Figurines		
	Price Paid	Value
1.		
2.		
3.		
4.		
5.		
6.		
7.		
8.		
9.		
10.		
Totals		

1 #912921

Carolyn
"Wishing You All Good Things"
Issued: 1993
Suspended: 1996 • Retired: 1996
Original Price: $22.50
Value by Year Mark:
3–$64 4–$53 5–$42 6–$35

2 #141321

Carrie
"The Future Beareth All Things"
Issued: 1995 • Retired: 1998
Original Price: $18.50
Value by Year Mark:
5–$39 6–$28 7–$25 8–$22

3 #706779

Cassandra
"Ghostly Greetings"
Issued: 2000 • Current
Original Price: $25
Value by Year Mark:
9–$25 I–$25 II–$25

4 #269980

Cathy
"An Autumn Breeze Blows Blessings To Please"
Issued: 1997 • Current
Original Price: $25
Value by Year Mark:
7–$33 8–$28 9–$25 I–$25 II–$25

5 #679089

Cecilia
(Gift To Go, sold as set)
"You Pull At My Heartstrings"
Issued: 2000 • Closed: 2000
Original Price: $30
Value by Year Mark: 9–$33 I–$33

6 #601578

Charissa & Ashylynn
"Every Journey Begins With One Step"
Issued: 1999 • Current
Original Price: $25
Value by Year Mark:
8–$25 9–$25 I–$25 II–$25

7 #910678

Charity
"I Found A Friend In Ewe"
Issued: 1993
Suspended: 1994 • Retired: 1996
Original Price: $20
Value by Year Mark:
LETTER–$200 3–$170

8 #950742

Charlie
"The Spirit Of Friendship Warms The Heart"
Issued: 1992
Suspended: 1996 • Retired: 1996
Original Price: $22.50
Value by Year Mark:
LETTER–$75 3–$65 4–$60 5–$51

9 #910694

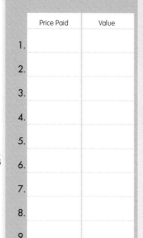

Chelsea
"Good Friends Are A Blessing"
Issued: 1993
Suspended: 1995 • Retired: 1995
Original Price: $15
Value by Year Mark:
LETTER–$295 3–$245 4–$235

10 #476633

Cherish
"Reach Out To Someone Around You"
Issued: 1999 • Current
Original Price: $12.50
Value by Year Mark:
8–$20 9–$15 I–$12.50 II–$12.50

Figurines

	Price Paid	Value
1.		
2.		
3.		
4.		
5.		
6.		
7.		
8.		
9.		
10.		

Totals

Figurines

1 #721174

"Cherish This Birthday Forever" (International Exclusive)
Issued: 2000 • Current
Original Price: $17.50
Value by Year Mark:
I–$17.50 II–$17.50

2 #CRT109

Cherished Teddies Town Sign (1995 Event Exclusive)
Issued: 1995 • Closed: 1995
Original Price: $6
Value: $20

3 #141216

Cheryl and Carl
"Wishing You A Cozy Christmas"
Issued: 1996 • Retired: 1998
Original Price: $25
Value by Year Mark:
6–$38 7–$31 8–$29

4 #103837

Christian
"My Prayer Is For You"
Issued: 1995 • Current
Original Price: $18.50
Value by Year Mark:
4–$35 5–$32 6–$27 7–$22 8–$20
9–$18.50 I–$18.50 II–$18.50

5 #103845

Christine
"My Prayer Is For You"
Issued: 1995 • Current
Original Price: $18.50
Value by Year Mark:
4–$35 5–$32 6–$27 7–$22 8–$20
9–$18.50 I–$18.50 II–$18.50

6 #707317

Christmas Mini Figurine
Boy With Overalls And Santa Hat
Issued: 2000 • Current
Original Price: $6
Value: $6

7 #707368

Christmas Mini Figurine
Christmas Tree Accessory
Issued: 2000 • Current
Original Price: $10
Value: $10

8 #707341

Christmas Mini Figurine
Dad Holding Hanging Ornament
Issued: 2000 • Current
Original Price: $6
Value: $6

9 #707333

Christmas Mini Figurine
Girl With Bowl And Spoon
Issued: 2000 • Current
Original Price: $6
Value: $6

10 #707309

Christmas Mini Figurine
Girl With Gingerbread Doll
Issued: 2000 • Current
Original Price: $6
Value: $6

Figurines

	Price Paid	Value
1.		
2.		
3.		
4.		
5.		
6.		
7.		
8.		
9.		
10.		
Totals		

Figurines

1 #707325

Christmas Mini Figurine
Girl Wrapping Gift
Issued: 2000 • Current
Original Price: $6
Value: $6

2 #707295

Christmas Mini Figurine
Santa Boy Sitting With Toy
Issued: 2000 • Current
Original Price: $6
Value: $6

3 #950483

Christopher
"Old Friends Are The Best Friends"
Issued: 1992 • Current
Original Price: $50
Value by Year Mark: *LETTER*–$109
3–$80 **4**–$68 **5**–$60 **6**–$53 **7**–$50
8–$50 **9**–$50 **I**–$50 **II**–$50

4 #128023

Christy
"Take Me To Your Heart"
Issued: 1995 • Retired: 1996
Original Price: $12.50
Value by Year Mark:
4–$45 **5**–$36 **6**–$32
Variation: white ribbon with blue dots
Value by Year Mark: **5**–$52

5 #666718

New

"Circle Of Love"
(Syndicated Catalog Exclusive)
Issued: 2001 • Current
Original Price: $37.50
Value by Year Mark:
I–$37.50 **II**–$37.50

6 #759511

Collecting Cherished Friends Along The Way (Homecoming Weekend Collector Figurine, sold as set w/pin, LE-10,000)
Issued: 2000 • Closed: 2000
Original Price: $50
Value: N/E
Variation: International Version, (LE-8,000), #759511I
Value: N/E

7 #912794

Connie
"You're A Sweet Treat"
Issued: 1993
Suspended: 1996 • Retired: 1996
Original Price: $15
Value by Year Mark:
3–$46 **4**–$37 **5**–$32

8 #819727

Constable Mackenzie (Canadian Exclusive)
"I'd Stand Watch For You Morning, Noon And Night"
Issued: 2000 • Current
Original Price: N/E
Value by Year Mark: **I**–N/E **II**–N/E

9 #916390

Courtney
"Springtime Is A Blessing From Above"
Issued: 1994
Suspended: 1995 • Retired: 1996
Original Price: $15
Value by Year Mark:
3–$152 **4**–$130 **5**–$110

10 #789585

New

Cynthia, Ethel, Nanette, Lola, Opal & Janel
"Love Passes From Generation To Generation"
Issued: 2001 • Current
Original Price: $50
Value by Year Mark: **I**–$50 **II**–$50

Figurines

	Price Paid	Value
1.		
2.		
3.		
4.		
5.		
6.		
7.		
8.		
9.		
10.		
Totals		

Figurines

1 #910651

Daisy
"Friendship Blossoms With Love"
Issued: 1993
Suspended: 1995 • Retired: 1996
Original Price: $15
Value by Year Mark:
LETTER–$825 **3**–$745

2 #597392

Daisy & Chelsea
(1999 Event Exclusive)
"Old Friends Always Find Their Way Back"
Issued: 1999 • Closed: 1999
Original Price: $20 (w/purchase)
Value by Year Mark: **9**–$35

3 #176214

Daniel
"You're My Little Pumpkin"
Issued: 1996 • Retired: 1998
Original Price: $22.50
Value by Year Mark:
6–$42 **7**–$30 **8**–$26

4 #265780

Danielle, Sabrina, Tiffany
(1997 Adoption Center
Exclusive, LE-25,000)
"We're Three Of A Kind"
Issued: 1997 • Closed: 1997
Original Price: $35
Value: $75
Variation: International Exclusive,
LE-17,500, #265780F
Value: $85

5 #676861

New

Danny
(Special Issue)
"You're The Finest Friend In The Forest"
Issued: 2001 • Current
Original Price: $22.50
Value by Year Mark:
I–$22.50 **II**–$22.50

6 #784974

Photo Unavailable

Darren (sold as set w/stocking)
Issued: 2000 • Retired: 2000
Original Price: N/A
Value by Year Mark: **I**–N/E

Figurines

	Price Paid	Value
1.		
2.		
3.		
4.		
5.		
6.		
7.		
8.		
9.		
10.		

Totals

7 #739049

New

Dawn
"You Don't Have To Search Far To Find Your Rainbow"
Issued: 2001 • Current
Original Price: $20
Value by Year Mark: **I**–$20 **II**–$20

8 #156361

Debbie
"Let's Hear It For Friendship!"
Issued: 1996 • Current
Original Price: $15
Value by Year Mark: **6**–$29 **7**–$22
8–$17 **9**–$15 **I**–$15 **II**–$15

9 #302694

"A Decade Of Teddy Bear Love"
Issued: 1998 • Current
Original Price: $30
Value by Year Mark:
7–$32 **8**–$30 **9**–$30 **I**–$30 **II**–$30

10 #476536

New

Delia
"You're The Beary Best Babysitter"
Issued: 2001 • Current
Original Price: $20
Value by Year Mark: **I**–$20 **II**–$20

1 #510963

**Dennis
(1999 Event Exclusive)**
"You Put The Spice In My Life"
Issued: 1999 • Closed: 1999
Original Price: $17.50
Value by Year Mark: **9**–$32

2 #848522

New

Dennis And Barb
"I Knew I Would Fall For You"
Issued: 2001 • Current
Original Price: $25
Value by Year Mark: **I**–$25 **II**–$25

3 #789658

New

Destiny And Kay
*"You've Never Look ed More
Beautiful Than You Do Today"*
Issued: 2001 • Current
Original Price: $25
Value by Year Mark: **I**–$25 **II**–$25

4 #786845

New

**Diana (Adoption
Center Exclusive)**
"I Cherish Your Bear Hugs"
Issued: 2001 • Current
Original Price: $13.50
Value by Year Mark:
I–$13.50 **II**–$13.50

5 #103799

Donald
*"Friends Are Egg-ceptional
Blessings"*
Issued: 1995
Suspended: 1995 • Retired: 1998
Original Price: $20
Value by Year Mark:
4–$46 **5**–$36 **6**–$29 **7**–$26 **8**–$22

6 #476730

Donna (U.K. Exclusive)
*"You've Sailed Straight
Into My Heart"*
Issued: 1999 • Current
Original Price: N/A
Value by Year Mark:
9–$47 **I**–$42 **II**–N/E

7 #797154

New

**Doris (sold as set
w/phone gift assortment)**
"I Just Called To Say I Love You"
Issued: 2001 • Current
Original Price: $25
Value by Year Mark: **I**–$25 **II**–$25

8 #128023

Dorothy
"Love Me True"
Issued: 1995 • Retired: 1996
Original Price: $12.50
Value by Year Mark:
4–$54 **5**–$40 **6**–$31
*Variation: white ribbon with
yellow dots*
Value by Year Mark: **5**–$60

9 #950661

Douglas
"Let's Be Friends"
Issued: 1992
Suspended: 1995 • Retired: 1995
Original Price: $20
Value by Year Mark:
LETTER–$102 **3**–$78 **4**–$63

10 #864234

New

Photo
Unavailable

**Drew (Cherished Retailer
Exclusive, LE-2001)**
*"Being Surrounded By My
Favorite Things Always Makes
Things Better"*
Issued: 2001 • To Be Closed: 2001
Original Price: $40
Value by Year Mark: **I**–$40 **II**–$40

Figurines		
	Price Paid	Value
1.		
2.		
3.		
4.		
5.		
6.		
7.		
8.		
9.		
10.		
Totals		

Figurines

1 #163473

**Duncan
(International Exclusive)**
*"Your Friendship Is Music
To My Ears"*
Issued: 1995 • Current
Original Price: 17.50
Value by Year Mark: **5**–$66 **6**–$48
7–$37 **8**–N/E **9**–N/E **I**–N/E **II**–N/E

2 #131873

Earl
"Warm-Hearted Friends"
Issued: 1995 • Retired: 1998
Original Price: $17.50
Value by Year Mark:
5–$39 **6**–$30 **7**–$25 **8**–$22

3 #466220

**Ed (1999 Gift
Show Exclusive)**
*"There's A Patch In My
Heart For You"*
Issued: 1999 • Closed: 1999
Original Price: $20
Value by Year Mark: **9**–$29

4 #867470

New

**Edna (Homecoming
Weekend Collector
Figurine)**
*"The Leaves Of Change Bring
Back The Fondest Memories"*
Issued: 2001 • To Be Closed: 2001
Original Price: $45
Value by Year Mark: **I**–$45 **II**–$45
Variation: red crystal heart
Value: N/E

5 #916277

Elizabeth & Ashley
"My Beary Best Friend"
Issued: 1994
Suspended: 1995 • Retired: 1996
Original Price: $25
Value by Year Mark: **3**–$73 **4**–$60

6 #622796

Eric
"Bear Tidings Of Joy"
Issued: 1994 • Retired: 1998
Original Price: $22.50
Value by Year Mark:
4–$46 **5**–$40 **6**–$35 **7**–$32 **8**–$30

7 #176028

Erica
*"Friends Are Always
Pulling For You"*
Issued: 1996 • Retired: 2000
Original Price: $22.50
Value by Year Mark:
6–$33 **7**–$27 **8**–$24 **9**–$24 **I**–$24

8 #203068

Erin
*"My Irish Eyes Smile
When You're Near"*
Issued: 1998 • Current
Original Price: $15
Value by Year Mark:
7–$25 **8**–$20 **9**–$15 **I**–$15 **II**–$15

9 #789623

Ernestine And Regina
*"I've Never Been More Proud Of
You Than I Am Today"*
Issued: 2000 • Current
Original Price: $25
Value by Year Mark: **I**–$25 **II**–$25

Figurines		
	Price Paid	Value
1.		
2.		
3.		
4.		
5.		
6.		
7.		
8.		
9.		
Totals		

1 #805580

New

Esther
*"I'm Surrounded By
Special Friends"*
Issued: 2001 • Current
Original Price: $17.50
Value by Year Mark:
I–$17.50 II–$17.50

2 #864293

New

Ethan
*"As Long As The Star Shines,
I Shall Follow It"*
Issued: 2001 • Current
Original Price: $20
Value by Year Mark: I–$20 II–$20

3 #484822

Evan (NALED Exclusive)
*"May Your Christmas Be
Trimmed In Happiness"*
Issued: 1999 • Closed: 1999
Original Price: $27.50
Value by Year Mark: 9–$30

4 #706787

New

Eve (LE-2001)
*"Everyone Needs Someone
To Watch Over Them"*
Issued: 2001 • To Be Closed: 2001
Original Price: $45
Value by Year Mark: II–$45

5 #916412

Faith
"There's No Bunny Like You"
Issued: 1994 • Suspended: 1995
Original Price: $20
Value by Year Mark:
3–$70 4–$58 5–$52

6 #867489

New

**Fay (American Cancer
Society® Exclusive)**
*"An Angel's Touch Is
Never Far Away"*
Issued: 2001 • Current
Original Price: $22.50
Value by Year Mark:
I–$22.50 II–$22.50

7 #476684

Fay & Arlene
*"Thanks For Always
Being By My Side"*
Issued: 1999 • Current
Original Price: $25
Value by Year Mark:
8–$25 9–$25 I–$25 II–$25

8 #601640

**Felix (German Design Your
Own Contest Winner)**
"Dër Glucksbringer"
Issued: 1999 • Current
Original Price: N/A
Value by Year Mark:
9–$60 I–$48 II–N/E

9 #476501

Leo

Scott   Tim   Dot

**Follow The Yellow Brick Road Collector Set
(set/5, LE-1999)**
Issued: 1999 • Closed: 1999
Original Price: $75
Value by Year Mark: 8–$88 9–$83

	Price Paid	Value
Figurines		
1.		
2.	10⁰⁰	20⁰⁰
3.		
4.		
5.		
6.		
7.		
8.		
9.		
Totals		

Figurines

1 #302716

"Forever Yours, Forever True"
Issued: 1998 • Current
Original Price: $30
Value by Year Mark:
7–$38 8–$33 9–I–$30 II–$30

2 #352950

Frank And Helen (1998 Catalog Exclusive)
"Snow One Like You"
Issued: 1998 • Closed: 1998
Original Price: $22.50
Value by Year Mark: 8–$48
Variation: International Exclusive, #352950I
Value: $58

3 #911747

Freda And Tina
"Our Friendship Is A Perfect Blend"
Issued: 1993 • Current
Original Price: $35
Value by Year Mark:
3–$62 4–$52 5–$62 6–$37 7–$35
8–$35 9–$35 I–$35 II–$35

4 #103772

Gail
"Catching The First Blossoms Of Friendship"
Issued: 1995
Suspended: 1995 • Retired: 1998
Original Price: $20
Value by Year Mark:
5–$43 6–$34 7–$26 8–$23

5 #912786

Gary
"Truest Friendships Are Scarce"
Issued: 1993 • Suspended: 1996
Original Price: $18.50
Value by Year Mark:
3–$46 4–$38 5–$31

6 #103640

Girl Cupid
"Be Mine"
Issued: 1995 • Suspended: 1995
Original Price: $15
Value by Year Mark: 4–$35

Figurines

	Price Paid	Value
1.		
2.		
3.		
4.		
5.		
6.		
7.		
8.		
9.		
10.		
Totals		

7 #103640

Girl Cupid
"Love"
Issued: 1995 • Suspended: 1995
Original Price: $15
Value by Year Mark: 4–$35

8 #833401

New

Girl With Stethescope
Issued: 2001 • Current
Original Price: $10
Value: $10

9 #477893

Glenn (LE-1999)
"By Land Or By Sea, Let's Go – Just You And Me"
Issued: 1999 • Closed: 1999
Original Price: $35
Value by Year Mark: 9–$46

10 #163465

Gordon (International Exclusive)
"Keepin' A Watchful Eye On You"
Issued: 1995 • Current
Original Price: $17.50
Value by Year Mark: 5–$58 6–$43
7–$36 8–N/E 9–N/E I–N/E II–N/E

1 #477907

**Graduation
(1999 Avon Exclusive)**
*"Always Put Your Best
Paw Forward"*
Issued: 1999 • Closed: 1999
Original Price: $12.99
Value by Year Mark: **9**–$25

2 #706930

New

**"Great Friendships Make
A Soldier Stand Tall"**
Issued: 2001 • Current
Original Price: $17.50
Value by Year Mark:
I–$17.50 **II**–$17.50

3 #912778

Gretel
"We Make Magic, Me And You"
Issued: 1993 • Retired: 1998
Original Price: $18.50
Value by Year Mark: **3**–$47 **4**–$38
5–$32 **6**–$26 **7**–$20 **8**–$20

4 #302651

"Growing Better Each Year"
Issued: 1998 • Current
Original Price: $22.50
Value by Year Mark:
8–$22.50 **9**–$22.50 **I**–$22.50 **II**–$22.50

5 #864285

New

Guy
*"I Come Bearing Gifts
For Everyone"*
Issued: 2001 • Current
Original Price: $17.50
Value by Year Mark:
I–$17.50 **II**–$17.50

6 #534145

Haley and Logan
*"Sisters And Hugs Soothe
The Soul"*
Issued: 1999 • Current
Original Price: $25
Value by Year Mark:
8–$29 **9**–$25 **I**–$25 **II**–$25

7 #152382

Halloween House
Issued: 1995 • Current
Original Price: $20
Value: $20

8 #176206

**Halloween Mini
Figurines (set/3)**
Issued: 1996 • Current
Original Price: $15
Value: $15

9 #912956

Hans
"Friends In Toyland"
Issued: 1993
Suspended: 1995 • Retired: 1995
Original Price: $20
Value by Year Mark: **3**–$105 **4**–$88

10 #911739

Harrison
"We're Going Places"
Issued: 1993 • Retired: 1997
Original Price: $15
Value by Year Mark:
3–$45 **4**–$38 **5**–$35 **6**–$32

Figurines

	Price Paid	Value
1.		
2.		
3.		
4.		
5.		
6.		
7.		
8.		
9.		
10.		
Totals		

Figurines

1 #676853

Harvey
(2000 Catalog Exclusive)
"I'm Surrounded By
Special Friends"
Issued: 2000 • Closed: 2000
Original Price: $20
Value by Year Mark: **9**–$36 **I**–$28

2 #534129

Hazel
"I've Got A Notion To Give
You A Potion"
Issued: 1999 • Retired: 1999
Original Price: $15
Value by Year Mark: **8**–$23 **9**–$23

3 #CRT240

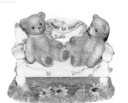

"Heart To Heart"
(1996 Event Exclusive)
Issued: 1996 • Closed: 1996
Original Price: $12.50
Value: $28

4 #476927

"Heaven Has Blessed This
Day" (Avon Exclusive)
Issued: 2000 • Closed: 2000
Original Price: $12.99
Value by Year Mark: **9**–$16 **I**–$16

5 #476919

"Heaven Has Blessed This
Day" (Avon Exclusive)
Issued: 2000 • Closed: 2000
Original Price: $12.99
Value by Year Mark: **9**–$16 **I**–$16

6 #910708

Heidi And David
"Special Friends"
Issued: 1993 • Suspended: 1995
Original Price: $25
Value by Year Mark:
LETTER–$65 **3**–$49 **4**–$40

7 #910686

Henrietta
"A Basketful Of Wishes"
Issued: 1993 • Suspended: 1994
Original Price: $22.50
Value by Year Mark:
LETTER–$175 **3**–$150

8 #916420

Henry
"Celebrating Spring With You"
Issued: 1994 • Suspended: 1995
Original Price: $20
Value by Year Mark: **3**–$53 **4**–$39

9 #916285

"Holding On To Someone
Special" (1993 Customer
Appreciation Exclusive)
Issued: 1993 • Closed: 1993
Original Price: $20
Value: $245

10 #534099

Honey
"You're A Good Friend That
Sticks Like Honey"
Issued: 1999 • Retired: 1999
Original Price: $16.50
Value by Year Mark: **8**–$22 **9**–$22

Figurines

	Price Paid	Value
1.		
2.		
3.		
4.		
5.		
6.		
7.		
8.		
9.		
10.		
Totals		

Figurines

1 #103764

Hope
"Our Love Is Ever-Blooming"
Issued: 1995
Suspended: 1995 • Retired: 1998
Original Price: $20
Value by Year Mark: 4–$39 5–$33
6–$27 7–$23 8–$22

2 #352977

Humphrey
(1998 Event Exclusive)
"Just The Bear Facts, Ma'am"
Issued: 1998 • Closed: 1998
Original Price: $15
Value by Year Mark: 8–$72

3 #354104

Hunter
"Me Cave Bear, You Friend"
Issued: 1998 • Retired: 1999
Original Price: $15
Value by Year Mark: 8–$29 9–$28

4 #739022

"Hurray! It's Your Birthday!"
(Limited Edition)
Issued: 2000 • Current
Original Price: $22.50
Value by Year Mark:
I–$22.50 II–$22.50

5 #797170

New

"I Just Called To Say I Love You" (sold as set w/tea cup, gift assortment)
Issued: 2001 • Current
Original Price: $25
Value by Year Mark: I–$25 II–$25

6 #542091

"I Love Hugs"
(Abbey Press Exclusive)
Issued: 1999 • Closed: 1999
Original Price: $15
Value by Year Mark: 8–$18 9–$18

7 #848530

New

Icabod
"Happy Hollow-ween!"
Issued: 2001 • Current
Original Price: $20
Value by Year Mark: I–$20 II–$20

8 #302988

"If A Mom's Love Comes In All Sizes, Yours Has The Biggest Of Hearts" (Gift To Go Exclusive, sold as set, #605344, w/mini figurine)
Issued: 1999 • Retired: 1999
Original Price: $25
Value by Year Mark: 9–$39

9 #617237

Ingrid (Dated 1994)
"Bundled-up With Warm Wishes"
Issued: 1994 • Closed: 1994
Original Price: $20
Value by Year Mark: 4–$58

10 #823295

Inspector Yukon
"I Will Always Keep You Safe And Protected"
Issued: 2000 • Current
Original Price: N/A
Value by Year Mark: I–N/E II–N/E

Figurines

	Price Paid	Value
1.		
2.		
3.		
4.		
5.		
6.		
7.		
8.		
9.		
10.		
Totals		

Figurines

1 #476404

Irene
"Time Leads Us Back To The Things We Love The Most"
Issued: 1999 • Current
Original Price: $20
Value by Year Mark:
8–$22 **9**–$20 **I**–$20 **II**–$20

2 #476943

Irish Mini Figurine (2 asst.)
Good Luck
Issued: 1999 • Current
Original Price: $7.50
Value: $7.50

3 #476943

Irish Mini Figurine (2 asst.)
Lucky Charm
Issued: 1999 • Current
Original Price: $7.50
Value: $7.50

4 #706728

Irmgard (Limited Edition)
"Your Smile Can Melt Any Heart"
Issued: 2000 • Current
Original Price: $25
Value by Year Mark: **I**–$25 **II**–$25

5 #707031

Isaac, Jeremiah & Temperance
"Faith Of Our Fathers"
Issued: 2000 • Current
Original Price: $30
Value by Year Mark: **I**–$30 **II**–$30

6 #745081

"It's A Boy!"
Issued: 2000 • Current
Original Price: $15
Value by Year Mark: **I**–$15 **II**–$15

Figurines

	Price Paid	Value
1.		
2.		
3.		
4.		
5.		
6.		
7.		
8.		
9.		
10.		
Totals		

7 #745073

"It's A Girl!"
Issued: 2000 • Current
Original Price: $15
Value by Year Mark: **I**–$15 **II**–$15

8 #950432

Jacki
"Hugs and Kisses"
Issued: 1992 • Current
Original Price: $10
Value by Year Mark:
LETTER–$45 **3**–$39 **4**–$30 **5**–$22 **6**–$17
7–$12 **8**–$10 **9**–$10 **I**–$10 **II**–$10
Variation: no dots on hairbow, dots on heart, patch on arm
Value: $65

9 #950734

Jacob
"Wishing For Love"
Issued: 1992 • Suspended: 1996
Original Price: $22.50
Value by Year Mark:
LETTER–$50 **3**–$45
4–$38 **5**–$35 **6**–$32

10 #141224

Jamie And Ashley
"I'm All Wrapped Up In Your Love"
Issued: 1996 • Retired: 1998
Original Price: $25
Value by Year Mark:
6–$46 **7**–$38 **8**–$32

Figurines

Figurines

1 #789666

New

Jan And Elise
"This Is The Start Of Your Bright And Exciting Future"
Issued: 2001 • Current
Original Price: $17.50
Value by Year Mark:
I–$17.50 II–$17.50

2 #203424

Jane (U.K. Frequent Buyer Program, Level 1)
"I'm All Washed Up Without You"
Issued: 1999 • Closed: 1999
Original Price: N/A
Value by Year Mark:
9–$80

3 #336521

Janet (1998 Avon Exclusive)
"You're Sweet As A Rose"
Issued: 1998 • Closed: 1998
Original Price: $19
Value by Year Mark: 8–$43
Variation: International Exclusive, #336521I
Value: N/E

4 #661910

New

Janice
"You Suit Me Perfectly"
Issued: 2001 • Current
Original Price: N/A
Value by Year Mark: I–N/E II–N/E

5 #202940

Jasmine (GCC Exclusive)
"A Bouquet Of Blessings For You"
Issued: 1999 • Closed: 1999
Original Price: $15
Value by Year Mark: 9–$31

6 #950475

Jasmine
"You Have Touched My Heart"
Issued: 1992 • Suspended: 1995
Original Price: $22.50
Value by Year Mark:
LETTER–$65 3–$52 4–$42

7 #269859

Jean (set/2)
"Cup Full Of Peace"
Issued: 1997 • Retired: 2000
Original Price: $25
Value by Year Mark:
7–$32 8–$27 9–$27 I–$27

8 #617091

Jedediah
"Giving Thanks For Friends"
Issued: 1994 • Retired: 1997
Original Price: $17.50
Value by Year Mark:
4–$46 5–$34 6–$28

9 #176044

Jeffrey (Dated 1996)
"Striking Up Another Year"
Issued: 1996 • Closed: 1996
Original Price: $17.50
Value by Year Mark: 6–$32

10 #103810

Jennifer
"Gathering The Blooms Of Friendship"
Issued: 1995
Suspended: 1995 • Retired: 1998
Original Price: $22.50
Value by Year Mark:
4–$43 5–$36 6–$28 7–$25 8–$25

Figurines

	Price Paid	Value
1.		
2.		
3.		
4.		
5.		
6.		
7.		
8.		
9.		
10.		
Totals		

Figurines

1 #950521

Jeremy
*"Friends Like You Are
Precious And True"*
Issued: 1992
Suspended: 1995 • Retired: 1995
Original Price: $15
Value by Year Mark:
LETTER–$66 **3**–$53 **4**–$46

2 #546534

**Jerome
(1999 Avon Exclusive)**
"Can't Bear The Cold Without You"
Issued: 1999 • Closed: 1999
Original Price: $14.99
Value by Year Mark: **9**–$33

3 #706655

**Jesse (Weekend Getaway
Event Exclusive)**
*"With You I'll Never Sing
The Country Blues"*
Issued: 2000 • Closed: 2000
Original Price: $17.50
Value by Year Mark:
I–N/E

4 #155438

Jessica
"A Mother's Heart Is Full Of Love"
Issued: 1997 • Retired: 1997
Original Price: $25
Value by Year Mark: **6**–$60 **7**–$46

5 #155438A

**Jessica
(1996 Catalog Exclusive)**
"A Mother's Heart Is Full Of Love"
Issued: 1996 • Closed: 1996
Original Price: $25
Value by Year Mark: **6**–$90

6 #269840

Joann (set/2)
"Cup Full Of Love"
Issued: 1997 • Retired: 2000
Original Price: $25
Value by Year Mark:
7–$30 **8**–$27 **9**–$27 **I**–$27

Figurines

	Price Paid	Value
1.		
2.		
3.		
4.		
5.		
6.		
7.		
8.		
9.		
10.		
Totals		

7 #476412

Joe
"Love Only Gets Better With Age"
Issued: 1999 • Current
Original Price: $15
Value by Year Mark:
8–$23 **9**–$15 **I**–$15 **II**–$15

8 #726621

**Joey And Lindsey
(Design Your Own
Contest Winner)**
*"We Can Weather Any
Storm Together"*
Issued: 2000 • Retired: 2000
Original Price: $30
Value by Year Mark: **9**–N/E **I**–N/E

9 #533858

John And William
*"When Friends Meet, Hearts
Warm"*
Issued: 1999 • Retired: 1999
Original Price: $35
Value by Year Mark: **8**–$38 **9**–$38

10 #911739

Jonathan
"Sail With Me"
Issued: 1993 • Retired: 1997
Original Price: $15
Value by Year Mark:
3–$48 **4**–$43 **5**–$36 **6**–$33

Figurines

1 #269832

Jordan (set/2)
"Cup Full Of Joy"
Issued: 1997 • Retired: 2000
Original Price: $25
Value by Year Mark:
7–$30 8–$27 9–$27 I–$27

2 #476471

Joseph
"Everyone Has Their Old Friends To Hug"
Issued: 1999 • Current
Original Price: $25
Value by Year Mark:
8–$30 9–$27 I–$27 II–$25

3 #805610

Josette
"You Are The Key To My Heart"
Issued: 1995 • Current
Original Price: $17.50
Value by Year Mark:
I–$17.50 II–$17.50

4 #950556

Joshua
"Love Repairs All"
Issued: 1992 • Retired: 1997
Original Price: $20
Value by Year Mark: LETTER–$48
3–$38 4–$33 5–$30 6–$25 7–$25

5 #506818

Jude
"Love Is The Beary Best Bedtime Story"
Issued: 2000 • Current
Original Price: $17.50
Value: $17.50

6 #534153

June And Jean
"I've Always Wanted To Be Just Like You"
Issued: 1999 • Current
Original Price: $20
Value by Year Mark:
8–$20 9–$20 I–$20 II–$20

7 #476641

Junior
"Everyone Is A Bear's Best Friend"
Issued: 1999 • Current
Original Price: $12.50
Value by Year Mark:
8–$20 9–$15 I–$12.50 II–$12.50

8 #537810

Justine And Janice
"Sisters And Friendship Are Crafted With Love"
Issued: 1999 • Current
Original Price: $25
Value by Year Mark:
8–$27 9–$25 I–$25 II–$25

9 #265799

Kara (1997 Adoption Center Event Exclusive)
"You're A Honey Of A Friend"
Issued: 1997 • Closed: 1997
Original Price: $15
Value by Year Mark: 7–$32

10 #950432

Karen
"Best Buddy"
Issued: 1992 • Current
Original Price: $10
Value by Year Mark:
LETTER–$47 3–$35 4–$29 5–$23 6–$14
7–$12 8–$10 9–$10 I–$10 II–$10
Variation: no dots on hairbow,
dots on heart, patch on arm
Value by Year Mark: 4–$85

Figurines		
	Price Paid	Value
1.		
2.		
3.		
4.		
5.		
6.		
7.		
8.		
9.		
10.		
Totals		

Figurines

1 New #874671

**Katherine
(Avon Exclusive)**
"You're The Best In The Business"
Issued: 2001 • Current
Original Price: $12.99
Value by Year Mark:
I–$12.99 II–$12.99

2 #916447

Kathleen
"Luck Found Me A Friend In You"
Issued: 1994 • Retired: 1999 △
Original Price: $12.50
Value by Year Mark: 3–$36 4–$33
5–$29 6–$24 7–$20 8–$16 9–$16

3 #950440

Katie
*"A Friend Always Knows
When You Need A Hug"*
Issued: 1992 • Retired: 1997
Original Price: $20
Value by Year Mark: *LETTER*–$65
3–$48 4–$37 5–$31 6–$28

4 #538299

**Katie, Renee, Jessica,
Matthew (1999 Gift
Show Exclusive)**
"I'm Surrounded By Hugs"
Issued: 1999 • Closed: 1999
Original Price: $25
Value by Year Mark: 9–$40
Variation: International Exclusive, #538299E
Value by Year Mark: 9–$50

5 #533815

**Kayla (1999 Gift Show
Exclusive)**
*"Big Hearts Come In
Small Packages"*
Issued: 1999 • Closed: 1999
Original Price: $20
Value by Year Mark: 9–$42

6 #354244

Keith and Deborah
"The Holidays Are Twice As Ice"
Issued: 1998 • Current
Original Price: $30
Value by Year Mark:
8–$38 9–$30 I–$30 II–$30

Figurines

	Price Paid	Value
1.		
2.		
3.		
4.		
5.	10.00	42.00
6.		
7.		
8.		
9.		
10.		

Totals

7 #916307

Kelly
"You're My One And Only"
Issued: 1994 • Suspended: 1995
Original Price: $15
Value by Year Mark: 3–$62 4–$52

8 #476692

**Kendra (U.K. Frequent
Buyer Program, Level 2)**
"Just The Bear Essentials"
Issued: 1999 • Closed: 1999
Original Price: N/A
Value by Year Mark: 9–$80

9 #103896

Kevin
"Good Luck To You"
Issued: 1995 • Retired: 1996
Original Price: $12.50
Value by Year Mark:
4–$40 5–$30 6–$27

10 #127965

**"Kiss The Hurt And
Make It Well"**
Issued: 1995 • Current
Original Price: $15
Value by Year Mark: 4–$35 5–$30
6–$19 7–$17 8–$15 9–$15 I–$15 II–$15

1 #131865

Kittie (1996 Adoption Center Event Exclusive)
"You Make Wishes Come True"
Issued: 1996 • Closed: 1996
Original Price: $17.50
Value by Year Mark: 6–$42
Variation: International Exclusive, #131865F
Value by Year Mark: 6–$58

2 #141194

Kristen
"Hugs Of Love And Friendship"
Issued: 1995 • Retired: 1998
Original Price: $20
Value by Year Mark:
5–$42 6–$31 7–$27 8–$22

3 #476390

Kyle
"Even Though We're Far Apart, You'll Always Have A Place In My Heart"
Issued: 1999 • Current
Original Price: $15
Value by Year Mark:
8–$15 9–$15 I–$15 II–$15

4 #337463

Lance (1998 Event Exclusive)
"Come Fly With Me"
Issued: 1998 • Closed: 1998
Original Price: $20
Value by Year Mark: 8–$38

5 #203440

Larry
"You're My Shooting Star"
Issued: 1997 • Current
Original Price: $17.50
Value by Year Mark: 7–$28 8–$23
9–$17.50 I–$17.50 II–$17.50

6 #156396

Laura
"Friendship Makes It All Better"
Issued: 1996 • Current
Original Price: $15
Value by Year Mark: 6–$26 7–$20
8–$18 9–$15 I–$15 II–$15

7 #272167

Lee (Dated 1997)
"You're A Bear's Best Friend"
Issued: 1997 • Closed: 1997
Original Price: $20
Value by Year Mark: 7–$36

8 #305979

Libby
"My Country 'Tis Of Thee"
Issued: 1998 • Retired: 1998
Original Price: $20
Value by Year Mark: 7–$44 8–$38

9 #742961
New

"Life Is Smooth Sailing With You"
Issued: 2001 • Current
Original Price: $17.50
Value by Year Mark:
I–$17.50 II–$17.50

10 #156426

Linda
"ABC And 1-2-3, You're A Friend To Me!"
Issued: 1996 • Current
Original Price: $15
Value by Year Mark: 6–$25 7–$20
8–$18 9–$15 I–$15 II–$15

Figurines	Price Paid	Value
1.		
2.		
3.		
4.		
5.		
6.		
7.		
8.		
9.		
10.		
Totals		

Figurines

1 #103780

Lisa
"My Best Is Always You"
Issued: 1995
Suspended: 1995 • Retired: 1998
Original Price: $20
Value by Year Mark:
4–$40 **5**–$34 **6**–$28 **7**–$25 **8**–$23

2 #103659

"Little Bundle Of Joy"
Issued: 1995 • Suspended: 1995
Original Price: $13.50
Value by Year Mark: **4**–$35

3 #103659

"Little Bundle Of Joy"
Issued: 1995 • Suspended: 1995
Original Price: $13.50
Value by Year Mark: **4**–$35

4 #666963

Loretta
(1999 Catalog Exclusive)
"I'm Warm And Cozy Over You"
Issued: 1999 • Closed: 1999
Original Price: $17.50
Value by Year Mark: **9**–$34

5 #476439

Lori
*"Those We Love Should
Be Cherished"*
Issued: 1999 • Current
Original Price: $17.50
Value by Year Mark:
8–$24 **9**–$17.50 **I**–$17.50 **II**–$17.50

6 #601608

**Lotje (Dutch Design Your
Own Contest Winner)**
"Sunday Morning Ride"
Issued: 1999 • Current
Original Price: N/A
Value by Year Mark:
9–$70 **I**–N/E **II**–N/E

Figurines

	Price Paid	Value
1.		
2.		
3.		
4.		
5.		
6.		
7.		
8.		
9.		
10.		
Totals		

7 #203432

Lou
"Take Me Out To The Ball Game"
Issued: 1998 • Current
Original Price: $15
Value by Year Mark:
7–$20 **8**–$17 **9**–$15 **I**–$15 **II**–$15

8 #661929

Lydia (Show Exclusive)
"You're The Bees Knees!"
Issued: 2000 • Closed: 2000
Original Price: $27.50
Value: $43

9 #310735

Lynn
"A Handmade Holiday Wish"
Issued: 1998 • Current
Original Price: $25
Value by Year Mark:
8–$30 **9**–$25 **I**–$25 **II**–$25

10 #310735A

Lynn
(1997 Catalog Exclusive)
"A Handmade Holiday Wish"
Issued: 1997 • Closed: 1997
Original Price: $25
Value by Year Mark: **7**–$42

Figurines

1 #135593

Madeline
"A Cup Full Of Friendship"
Issued: 1995 • Retired: 1999
Original Price: $20
Value by Year Mark: **4**–$35 **5**–$30
6–$26 **7**–$24 **8**–$24 **9**–$24

2 #950572

Mandy
"I Love You Just The Way You Are"
Issued: 1992
Suspended: 1995 • Retired: 1995
Original Price: $15
Value by Year Mark:
LETTER–$66 **3**–$56 **4**–$44

3 #103667

Margaret
"A Cup Full Of Love"
Issued: 1995 • Retired: 1999
Original Price: $20
Value by Year Mark: **4**–$35 **5**–$30
6–$26 **7**–$24 **8**–$24 **9**–$24

4 #475602

Margy
(1998 Avon Exclusive)
*"I'm Wrapping Up A Little
Holiday Joy To Send Your Way"*
Issued: 1998 • Closed: 1998
Original Price: $19.99
Value by Year Mark: **8**–$42

5 #910767

Marie
"Friendship Is A Special Treat"
Issued: 1993 • Retired: 1999
Original Price: $20
Value by Year Mark:
LETTER–$60 **3**–$50 **4**–$46 **5**–$40
6–$30 **7**–$27 **8**–$24 **9**–$24
Variation: blue napkin, white hearts on teapot
Value: $80

6 #135682

Marilyn
"A Cup Full Of Cheer"
Issued: 1995 • Retired: 1999
Original Price: $20
Value by Year Mark: **4**–$35 **5**–$30
6–$24 **7**–$24 **8**–$24 **9**–$24

7 #368164

**Marlene & Marissa
(Cherished Memories
Promotional Figurine)**
*"Good Friends Are Always
Beary Near"*
Issued: 1999 • Closed: 1999
Original Price: N/A
Value by Year Mark: **9**–$100

8 #912840

Mary
*"A Special Friend Warms
The Season"*
Issued: 1993 • Retired: 2000
Original Price: $25
Value by Year Mark: **3**–$53 **4**–$45
5–$39 **6**–$32 **7**–$28 **8**–$26 **9**–$26 **I**–$26

9 #805572

**Matilda
(Australian Exclusive)**
*"We're All Cheering For
You In 2000"*
Issued: 2000 • Current
Original Price: N/A
Value by Year Mark:
9–$46 **I**–$46 **II**–N/E

10 #476781

Matt and Vicki (LE-1999)
*"Love Is The Best Thing
Two Can Share"*
Issued: 1999 • Closed: 1999
Original Price: $35
Value by Year Mark: **9**–$54

	Figurines	
	Price Paid	Value
1.		
2.		
3.		
4.		
5.		
6.		
7.		
8.		
9.		
10.		
	Totals	

Figurines

1 #135690

Maureen
"Lucky Friend"
Issued: 1995
Suspended: 1995 • Retired: 1996
Original Price: $12.50
Value by Year Mark: **4**–$35 **5**–$30

2 #103829

Melissa
"Every Bunny Needs A Friend"
Issued: 1995
Suspended: 1995 • Retired: 1998
Original Price: $20
Value by Year Mark: **4**–$42 **5**–$38
6–$27 **7**–$22 **8**–$22

3 #534226

Meredith
"You're As Cozy As A
Pair Of Mittens!"
Issued: 1999 • Current
Original Price: $10
Value by Year Mark:
8–$10 **9**–$10 **I**–$10 **II**–$10

4 #910775

Michael and Michelle
"Friendship Is A Cozy Feeling"
Issued: 1993 • Suspended: 1995
Original Price: $30
Value by Year Mark:
LETTER–$80 **3**–$66 **4**–$56
Variation: yellow ruffle
Value: $85

5 #356255

Mike (1998 Adoption
Center Event Exclusive)
"I'm Sweet On You"
Issued: 1998 • Closed: 1998
Original Price: $15
Value by Year Mark: **7**–$35 **8**–$35

6 #912751

Miles
"I'm Thankful For A
Friend Like You"
Issued: 1993 • Retired: 1998
Original Price: $17
Value by Year Mark: **3**–$42 **4**–$34
5–$26 **6**–$22 **7**–$22 **8**–$22

Figurines

	Price Paid	Value
1.		
2.		
3.		
4.		
5.		
6.		
7.		
8.		
9.		
10.		
Totals		

7 #128023

Millie
"Love Me Tender"
Issued: 1995 • Retired: 1996
Original Price: $12.50
Value by Year Mark:
4–$60 **5**–$43 **6**–$30
Variation: white ribbon with violet dots
*Value by Year Mark: **5**–$55*

8 #534137

Milt And Garrett
"A-Haunting We Will Go"
Issued: 1999 • Retired: 1999
Original Price: $20
Value by Year Mark: **8**–$26 **9**–$26

9 #542644

Milton (Millennium
Event Figurine)
"Wishing For A Future As
Bright As The Stars"
Issued: 1999 • Closed: 2000
Original Price: $20
Value by Year Mark: **9**–$35 **I**–$28

10 #786578

New

Mimi, Darcie And Misty
"There's Always Time For Friends
... And A Good Cup Of Tea"
Issued: 2001 • Current
Original Price: $45
Value by Year Mark: **I**–$45 **II**–$45

1 #156418

Mindy
*"Friendship Keeps Me
On My Toes"*
Issued: 1996 • Current
Original Price: $15
Value by Year Mark: 6–$24 7–$18
8–$15 9–$15 I–$15 II–$15

2 #910759

Molly
"Friendship Softens A Bumpy Ride"
Issued: 1993
Suspended: 1995 • Retired: 1996
Original Price: $30
Value by Year Mark:
LETTER–$75 3–$65 4–$55

3 #154016

Mother Goose And Friends
*"Friends Of A Feather
Flock Together"*
Issued: 1998 • Current
Original Price: $50
Value by Year Mark:
7–$55 8–$50 9–$50 I–$50 II–$50

4 #503711

Mother's Day Mini Figurines
"Grandma"
Issued: 1999 • Current
Original Price: $7.50
Value: $7.50

5 #476773

Mother's Day Mini Figurines
"Mom"
Issued: 1999 • Current
Original Price: $7.50
Value: $7.50

6 #503738

Mother's Day Mini Figurines
"Nana"
Issued: 1999 • Current
Original Price: $7.50
Value: $7.50

7 #916315

Nancy
*"Your Friendship Makes
My Heart Sing"*
Issued: 1994
Suspended: 1995 • Retired: 1996
Original Price: $15
Value by Year Mark:
3–$120 4–$118

8 #534110

Natalie
*"You Make Me Smile
From Ear To Ear"*
Issued: 1999 • Retired: 1999
Original Price: $15
Value by Year Mark: 8–$25 9–$22

9 #176222

Nathan
"Leave Your Worries Behind"
Issued: 1998 • Current
Original Price: $17.50
Value by Year Mark:
8–$17.50 9–$17.50 I–$17.50 II–$17.50

10 #950513

Nathaniel And Nellie
"It's Twice As Nice With You"
Issued: 1992 • Retired: 1996
Original Price: $30
Value by Year Mark:
LETTER–$82 3–$65 4–$56 5–$50

Figurines

	Price Paid	Value
1.		
2.		
3.		
4.		
5.		
6.		
7.		
8.		
9.		
10.		
Totals		

Figurines

1 #272361

Newton
"Ringing In The New Year With Cheer"
Issued: 1997 • Current
Original Price: $15
Value by Year Mark:
7–$24 8–$19 9–$15 I–$15 II–$15

2 #534218

Nikki
"A Cold Winter's Day Won't Keep Me Away"
Issued: 1999 • Current
Original Price: $10
Value by Year Mark:
8–$10 9–$10 I–$10 II–$10

3 #617245

Nils
"Near And Deer For Christmas"
Issued: 1994
Suspended: 1996 • Retired: 1997
Original Price: $22.50
Value by Year Mark: 4–$70 5–$56

4 #215864

Nina
(1997 Event Exclusive)
"Beary Happy Wishes"
Issued: 1997 • Closed: 1997
Original Price: $17.50
Value by Year Mark: 7–$34

5 #534188

Norbit And Nyla
(Dated 1999)
"A Friend Is Someone Who Reaches For Your Hand And Touches Your Heart"
Issued: 1999 • Closed: 1999
Original Price: $25
Value by Year Mark: 9–$43

6 #476765

Norm
"Patience Is A Fisherman's Virtue"
Issued: 1999 • Current
Original Price: $25
Value by Year Mark:
8–$36 9–$25 I–$25 II–$25

Figurines

	Price Paid	Value
1.		
2.		
3.		
4.		
5.		
6.		
7.		
8.		
9.		
10.		
Totals		

7 #706639

Norma (Regional Event Exclusive)
"We'll Share Secrets Until The Wee Hours"
Issued: 2000 • Closed: 2000
Original Price: gift w/ticket
Value: $63

8 #822353

NSPCC Figure
Issued: 2000 • Current
Original Price: N/A
Value by Year Mark: I–N/E II–N/E

9 #182966

Olga (LE-1996)
"Feel The Peace . . . Hold The Joy . . . Share The Love"
Issued: 1996 • Closed: 1996
Original Price: $50
Value by Year Mark: 6–$70

10 #916641

Oliver & Olivia
"Will You Be Mine?"
Issued: 1994 • Suspended: 1995
Original Price: $25
Value by Year Mark: 3–$75 4–$64

1 #786586

New

Palmer And Charlene
"Clowning Around"
Issued: 2001 • Current
Original Price: $25
Value by Year Mark: I–$25 II–$25

2 #141313

Pat
"Falling For You"
Issued: 1995 • Current
Original Price: $22.50
Value by Year Mark:
5–$40 6–$28 7–$24
8–$22.50 9–$22.50 I–$22.50 II–$22.50
Variation: blue shirt on doll
Value by Year Mark: 5–$48

3 #617105

Patience
"Happiness Is Homemade"
Issued: 1994 • Retired: 1997
Original Price: $17.50
Value by Year Mark:
4–$47 5–$33 6–$28

(4) #911429

Patrice
"Thank You For The Sky So Blue"
Issued: 1993 • Retired: 1999
Original Price: $18.50
Value by Year Mark:
LETTER–$68 3–$50 4–$43 5–$36
6–$28 7–$26 8–$24 9–$24
Variation: bunny with white tail
Value: $47

5 #911410

Patrick
*"Thank You For A Friend
That's True"*
Issued: 1993 • Retired: 1999
Original Price: $18.50
Value by Year Mark:
LETTER–$62 3–$50 4–$43 5–$38
6–$28 7–$26 8–$24 9–$24

6 #789631

New

Patty And Peggy
*"Spending Time With You
Is Priceless"*
Issued: 2001 • Current
Original Price: $25
Value by Year Mark: I–$25 II–$25

7 #466328

**Paul
(1999 Adoption Center
Exclusive, LE-35,000)**
*"Good Friends Warm The Heart
With Many Blessings"*
Issued: 1999 • Closed: 1999
Original Price: $22.50
Value by Year Mark: 9–$48
*Variation: International Exclusive, LE-
20,000, #4633281*
Value by Year Mark: 9–$59

8 #676888

New

**Paul Revere
(Special Issue)**
*"You Can Always Trust Me
To Be There"*
Issued: 2001 • Current
Original Price: $20
Value by Year Mark: I–$20 II–$20

9 #874728

New

Paula (Avon Exclusive)
*"Helping Others Is The Best Part
Of My Job"*
Issued: 2001
To Be Retired: 2001
Original Price: $12.99
Value by Year Mark:
I–$12.99 II–$12.99

10 #833444

Pauline
"A Woman's Work Is Never Done"
Issued: 2000 • Current
Original Price: $17.50
Value by Year Mark:
I–$17.50 II–$17.50

Figurines

	Price Paid	Value
1.		
2.		
3.		
4.	18 50	50 00
5.		
6.		
7.		
8.		
9.		
10.		

Totals

Figurines

1 #337579

**Penny, Chandler, Boots
(1998 Adoption Center
Exclusive, LE-25,000)**
"We're Inseparable"
Issued: 1998 • Closed: 1998
Original Price: $25
Value by Year Mark: **8**–$63
Variation: International Exclusive, LE-20,000, #337579F
Value by Year Mark: **8**–$60

2 #104973

Peter
"You're Some Bunny Special"
Issued: 1995
Suspended: 1995 • Retired: 1998
Original Price: $17.50
Value by Year Mark:
4–$38 **5**–$32 **6**–$23
7–$20 **8**–$20
Variation: dark eggs, narrow base
Value: $47

3 #617113

Phoebe
*"A Little Friendship Is
A Big Blessing"*
Issued: 1994 • Retired: 1995
Original Price: $13.50
Value by Year Mark: **4**–$60 **5**–$50

4 #910724

Priscilla
"Love Surrounds Our Friendship"
Issued: 1993 • Retired: 1997
Original Price: $15
Value by Year Mark:
LETTER–$72 **3**–$57 **4**–$45
5–$36 **6**–$29

5 N/A

New

**Priscilla And Clara
(Regional Show Exclusive)**
Issued: 2001 • Current
Original Price: N/A
Value by Year Mark: **I**–N/E **II**–N/E

6 #128031

**Priscilla & Greta
(set/2, LE-19,950)**
"Our Hearts Belong To You"
Issued: 1995 • Closed: 1996
Original Price: $50
Value: $110
*Variation: International Exclusive,
LE-10,000, #128031F*
Value: $125

Figurines

	Price Paid	Value
1.		
2.		
3.		
4.		
5.		
6.		
7.		
8.		
9.		
10.		

Totals

7 #CRT025

**Priscilla Ann
(1994-95 Expo Exclusive)**
"There's No One Like Hue"
Issued: 1994 • Closed: 1995
Original Price: $25
Value by Year Mark: **4**–$230

8 #912808

Prudence
"A Friend To Be Thankful For"
Issued: 1993 • Retired: 1998
Original Price: $17
Value by Year Mark:
3–$46 **4**–$35 **5**–$27
6–$22 **7**–$20 **8**–$19

9 #706841

Ralph
*"Bring Joy To Those
You Hold Deer"*
Issued: 2000 • Current
Original Price: $17.50
Value by Year Mark:
I–$17.50 **II**–$17.50

10 #476498

Randy
*"You're Never Alone With
Good Friends Around"*
Issued: 1999 • Current
Original Price: $22.50
Value by Year Mark:
8–$30 **9**–$22.50
I–$22.50 **II**–$22.50

Figurines

1 #269999

Rex
"Our Friendship Will Never Be Extinct"
Issued: 1997 • Current
Original Price: $17.50
Value by Year Mark:
7–$24 **8**–$19
9–$17.50 **I**–$17.50 **II**–$17.50

2 #352721

Rich (Dated 1998)
"Always Paws For Holiday Treats"
Issued: 1998 • Closed: 1998
Original Price: $22.50
Value by Year Mark: **8**–$44

3 #476617

Rita
(NALED Exclusive)
"Wishing You Love Straight From The Heart"
Issued: 1999 • Closed: 1999
Original Price: $17.50
Value by Year Mark: **9**–$40

4 #911402

Robbie And Rachel
"Love Bears All Things"
Issued: 1993 • Retired: 1999
Original Price: $27.50
Value by Year Mark:
3–$58 **4**–$48 **5**–$42 **6**–$35
7–$32 **8**–$32 **9**–$32

5 #156272

Robert
"Love Keeps Me Afloat"
Issued: 1996 • Retired: 1999
Original Price: $13.50
Value by Year Mark:
5–$38 **6**–$28 **7**–$17
8–$15 **9**–$15

6
New #789615

Roberta
"Being Your Friend Is My Favorite Pastime"
Issued: 2001 • Current
Original Price: $15
Value by Year Mark: **I**–$15 **II**–$15

7 #533882

Rodney
(Gift To Go Exclusive, sold as set, #646504, w/plush piece)
"I'm Santa's Little Helper"
Issued: 1999 • Retired: 1999
Original Price: $25
Value by Year Mark: **9**–$30

8 #706647

Ron (Adoption Center Exclusive, LE-25,000)
"Enjoy The Simple Comforts Of Life"
Issued: 2000 • Closed: 2000
Original Price: $20
Value by Year Mark: **I**–N/E **II**–N/E

9 #706981

Rosemarie And Ronald
"A Hug Is Worth A Thousand Words, A Friend Is Worth More"
Issued: 2000 • Current
Original Price: $27.50
Value by Year Mark:
I–$27.50 **II**–$27.50

10 #601586

Roxie & Shelly
"What A Story We Share!"
Issued: 1999 • Current
Original Price: $25
Value by Year Mark:
8–$25 **9**–$25 **I**–$25 **II**–$25

Figurines

	Price Paid	Value
1.		
2.		
3.		
4.		
5.		
6.		
7.		
8.		
9.		
10.		

Totals

Figurines

1 #466298

Roy
(1998 Gift Show Exclusive)
"I'm Your Country Cowboy"
Issued: 1998 • Closed: 1998
Original Price: $17.50
Value: $40

2 #476668

Ruth & Gene
*"Even When We Don't See
Eye To Eye, We're Always
Heart To Heart"*
Issued: 1999 • Current
Original Price: $25
Value by Year Mark:
8–$25 9–$25 I–$25 II–$25

3 #203041

Ryan
"I'm Green With Envy For You"
Issued: 1997 • Current
Original Price: $20
Value by Year Mark:
6–$30 7–$25 8–$20
9–$20 I–$20 II–$20

4 #510955

Sally & Skip
**(1999 Adoption Center
Exclusive, LE-25,000)**
"We Make A Perfect Team"
Issued: 1999 • Closed: 1999
Original Price: $27.50
Value: $48
*Variation: International Exclusive,
LE-20,000, #510955F*
Value: $65

5 #302619

Sam
"I Want You … To Be My Friend"
Issued: 1998 • Retired: 1998
Original Price: $17.50
Value by Year Mark: 7–$42 8–$36

6 #950432

Sara
"Love Ya"
Issued: 1992 • Current
Original Price: $10
Value by Year Mark:
LETTER–$52 3–$38 4–$30 5–$24
6–$20 7–$12 8–$10 9–$10 I–$10 II–$10
*Variation: no dots on hairbow,
dots on heart, patch on arm
Value by Year Mark: 4–$95*

Figurines

	Price Paid	Value
1.		
2.		
3.	'	
4.		
5.		
6.		
7.		
8.		
9.		
10.		
Totals		

7 #916439

Sean
"Luck Found Me A Friend In You"
Issued: 1994 • Retired: 1999 Δ
Original Price: $12.50
Value by Year Mark:
3–$40 4–$33 5–$24 6–$20
7–$15 8–$15 9–$15

8 #534102

Sedley
*"We've Turned Over A New Leaf
On Our Friendship"*
Issued: 1999 • Current
Original Price: $16.50
Value by Year Mark:
8–$19 9–$16.50 I–$16.50 II–$16.50

9 #352799

Segrid, Justaf & Ingmar
(LE-1998)
*"The Spirit Of Christmas
Grows In Our Hearts"*
Issued: 1998 • Closed: 1998
Original Price: $45
Value by Year Mark: 8–$72

10 #103551

"Sent With Love"
Issued: 1995 • Suspended: 1995
Original Price: $17.50
Value by Year Mark: 4–$36

Figurines

1 #128015

Seth And Sarabeth
"We're Beary Good Pals"
Issued: 1995 • Retired: 1999
Original Price: $25
Value by Year Mark:
4–$52 5–$39 6–$30
7–$27 8–$27 9–$27

2 #354260

Shannon
"A Figure 8, Our Friendship Is Great!"
Issued: 1998 • Current
Original Price: $20
Value by Year Mark:
8–$26 9–$20 I–$20 II–$20

3 #163481

Sherlock (International Exclusive)
"Good Friends Are Hard To Find"
Issued 1995 • Current
Original Price: $17.50
Value by Year Mark:
5–$62 6–$42 7–$34
8–N/E 9–N/E I–N/E II–N/E

4 #805564

Sidney (Australian Exclusive)
"We're All Cheering For You In 2000"
Issued: 2000 • Current
Original Price: N/A
Value by Year Mark:
9–$45 I–N/E II–N/E

5 #466271

Sierra (1998 Gift Show Exclusive)
"You're My Partner"
Issued: 1998 • Closed: 1998
Original Price: $17.50
Value: $41

6 #601551

Simone & Jhodi
"I've Always Believed In You"
Issued: 1999 • Current
Original Price: $25
Value by Year Mark:
8–$25 9–$25 I–$25 II–$25

7 #302643

"Sixteen Candles And Many More Wishes"
Issued: 1998 • Current
Original Price: $22.50
Value by Year Mark:
7–$24 8–$22.50
9–$22.50 I–$22.50 II–$22.50

8 #742988

New

"The Sky's The Limit"
Issued: 2001 • Current
Original Price: $17.50
Value by Year Mark:
I–$17.50 II–$17.50

9 #601594

Skylar & Shana
"When You Find A Sunbeam, Share The Warmth"
Issued: 1999 • Current
Original Price: $25
Value by Year Mark:
8–$25 9–$25 I–$25 II–$25

10 #622818

Sonja
"Holiday Cuddles"
Issued: 1994 • Retired: 1998
Original Price: $20
Value by Year Mark:
4–$42 5–$32 6–$24
7–$22 8–$22

Figurines

	Price Paid	Value
1.		
2.		
3.		
4.		
5.		
6.		
7.		
8.		
9.		
10.		
Totals		

Figurines

1 #864307

New

Sonny (sold as set with knit stocking)
"Getting Ready For Santa's Visit"
Issued: 2001
To Be Retired: Dec. 24, 2001
Original Price: $22.50
Value by Year Mark:
I–$22.50 II–$22.50

2 #789879

New

Sparky
"Your Cheerful Ways Bring Better Days"
Issued: 2001 • Current
Original Price: $15
Value by Year Mark: I–$15 II–$15

3 #791403

New

Spring Bonnet Figurine (Avon Exclusive)
"Love Is The Poetry Of The Soul"
Issued: 2001
To Be Retired: 2001
Original Price: $7.99
Value: $7.99

4 #791349

New

Spring Bonnet Figurine (Avon Exclusive)
"Give Life A Hug"
Issued: 2001
To Be Retired: 2001
Original Price: $7.99
Value: $7.99

5 #791373

New

Spring Bonnet Figurine (Avon Exclusive)
"Friends Are The Spice Of Life"
Issued: 2001
To Be Retired: 2001
Original Price: $7.99
Value: $7.99

6 #916358

Spring Mini Figurine (3 asst.)
"Girl With Blue Bonnet And Duck"
Issued: 1994 • Current
Original Price: $7
Value: $7

7 #916358

Spring Mini Figurine (3 asst.)
"Girl With Daisy Headband"
Issued: 1994 • Current
Original Price: $7
Value: $7

8 #916358

Spring Mini Figurine (3 asst.)
"Girl With White Hat And Flower"
Issued: 1994 • Current
Original Price: $7
Value: $7

9 #617148

Stacie
"You Lift My Spirit"
Issued: 1994 • Retired: 1998
Original Price: $18.50
Value by Year Mark:
4–$48 5–$42 6–$30
7–$28 8–$24

10 #534250

Star (LE-1999)
"Cherish Yesterday, Dream Tomorrow, Live Today"
Issued: 1999 • Closed: 1999
Original Price: $55
Value by Year Mark: 9–$70

Figurines

	Price Paid	Value
1.		
2.		
3.		
4.		
5.		
6.		
7.		
8.		
9.		
10.		
Totals		

Figurines

1 #706795

Stella
"Touches Of Heaven Can Be Found On Earth"
Issued: 2000 • Current
Original Price: $22.50
Value by Year Mark:
I–$22.50 II–$22.50

2 #482544

New

Stephanie And Melanie
(set/3, Cherished Retailers
Exclusive, LE-10,000)
"Tea And Cookies Warm The Soul, But Close Friends Warm The Heart"
Issued: 2001 • To Be Closed: 2001
Original Price: $60
Value by Year Mark: I–$70 II–$65
Variation: International Exclusive, LE-3,000, #482544I
Value: N/E

3 #951129

Steven
"A Season Filled With Sweetness"
Issued: 1992 • Retired: 1995
Original Price: $20
Value by Year Mark:
LETTER–$85 3–$69 4–$63 5–$54

4 #706760

Sullivan
"The Most Important Truth Is To Be True To Yourself"
Issued: 2000 • Current
Original Price: $17.50
Value by Year Mark:
I–$17.50 II–$17.50

5 #272159

Sven and Liv (LE-1997)
"All Paths Lead To Kindness And Friendship"
Issued: 1997 • Closed: 1997
Original Price: $55
Value by Year Mark: 7–$77

6 #265810

Sylvia
(1997 Event Exclusive)
"A Picture Perfect Friendship"
Issued: 1997 • Closed: 1997
Original Price: $15
Value by Year Mark: 7–$65

7 #176257

Tabitha
"You're The Cat's Meow"
Issued: 1996 • Retired: 1998
Original Price: $15
Value by Year Mark:
6–$30 7–$25 8–$20

8 #510947

Tammy
(1999 Event Exclusive)
"Let's Go To The Hop!"
Issued: 1999 • Closed: 1999
Original Price: $15
Value by Year Mark: 9–$70

9 #601624

Tanner (Canadian Design Your Own Contest Winner)
"Friends Of Old Are Dear To Hold"
Issued: 1999
Out Of Production: 2000
Original Price: N/A
Value by Year Mark: 9–$46 I–$46

10 #156353

Tasha
(1996 Adoption Center Exclusive, LE-19,960)
"In Grandmother's Attic"
Issued: 1996 • Closed: 1996
Original Price: $55
Value by Year Mark: 6–$153
Variation: International Exclusive, LE-10,000, #156353F
Value: $225

Figurines

	Price Paid	Value
1.		
2.		
3.		
4.		
5.		
6.		
7.		
8.		
9.		
10.		

Totals

Figurines

1 #617156

Taylor
"Sail The Seas With Me"
Issued: 1994 • Suspended: 1996
Original Price: $15
Value by Year Mark:
4–$46 5–$38

2 #601632

Teaghan
(Australian Design Your
Own Contest Winner)
*"A Big Step To Start
You On Your Way"*
Issued: 1999
Out Of Production: 2000
Original Price: N/A
Value by Year Mark: 9–N/E I–$56

3 #476757

Teddy
"Friends Give You Wings To Fly"
Issued: 1999 • Current
Original Price: $15
Value by Year Mark:
8–$22 9–$15 I–$15 II–$15

4 #624918

Teddy And Roosevelt
(LE-1993)
"The Book Of Teddies 1903-1993"
Issued: 1993 • Closed: 1993
Original Price: $20
Value by Year Mark:
3–$198

5 #686999

Terry (sold as set
w/computer kit)
"Friendship Is More Than 9 To 5"
Issued: 2000 • Current
Original Price: $30
Value by Year Mark:
9–$30 I–$30 II–$30

6 #865095
New

Terry
*"Always Stay On Track About
The True Meaning Of Christmas"*
Issued: 2001 • Current
Original Price: $22.50
Value by Year Mark:
I–$22.50 II–$22.50

7 #617075

Thanksgiving Quilt
Issued: 1994
Out Of Production: 2000
Original Price: $12
Value: $13

8 #912883

Theadore, Samantha
And Tyler (9")
"Friendship Weathers All Storms"
Issued: 1993 • Suspended: 1995
Original Price: $160
Value by Year Mark:
3–$230 4–$205

9 #950505

Theadore, Samantha
And Tyler
"Friends Come In All Sizes"
Issued: 1992 • Current
Original Price: $20
Value by Year Mark:
LETTER–$80 3–$49 4–$40 5–$34 6–$25
7–$22 8–$20 9–$20 I–$20 II–$20
*Variation: Theadore with blue heart
patch*
Value by Year Mark: 4–$120

10 #950769

Theadore, Samantha
And Tyler
"Friendship Weathers All Storms"
Issued: 1992 • Retired: 1997
Original Price: $17
Value by Year Mark:
LETTER–$100 3–$80
4–$69 5–$56 6–$46

Figurines		
	Price Paid	Value
1.		
2.		
3.		
4.		
5.		
6.		
7.		
8.		
9.		
10.		
Totals		

Figurines

Figurines

1 #951196

Theadore, Samantha and Tyler (9")
"Friends Come In All Sizes"
Issued: 1992 • Retired: 1999
Original Price: $130
Value by Year Mark:
LETTER–$205 **3**–$180 **4**–$170 **5**–$166
6–$159 **7**–$155 **8**–$150 **9**–$143

2 #215910

"This Calls For A Celebration"
Issued: 1997 • Current
Original Price: $15
Value by Year Mark:
7–$20 **8**–$15 **9**–$15 **I**–$15 **II**–$15

3 #911739

Thomas
"Chuggin' Along"
Issued: 1993 • Retired: 1997
Original Price: $15
Value by Year Mark:
3–$54 **4**–$48 **5**–$36 **6**–$33

4 #910740

Timothy
"A Friend Is Forever"
Issued: 1993
Suspended: 1995 • Retired: 1996
Original Price: $15
Value by Year Mark:
LETTER–$68 **3**–$56 **4**–$43

5 #676845

New

Tori
"Friends Are The Sweetest Part Of Life"
Issued: 2001 • Current
Original Price: gift w/$25 purchase
Value by Year Mark: **I**–N/E **II**–N/E

6 #911372

Tracie And Nicole
"Side By Side With Friends"
Issued: 1993 • Retired: 1999
Original Price: $35
Value by Year Mark:
3–$70 **4**–$58 **5**–$52 **6**–$43
7–$40 **8**–$40 **9**–$40

7 #354112

Trevor
"You Bring Out The Devil In Me"
Issued: 1998 • Current
Original Price: $17.50
Value by Year Mark:
8–$20 **9**–$17.50 **I**–$17.50 **II**–$17.50

8 #864366

New

**Troy
(Adoption Center Exclusive)**
"Life's A Beach"
Issued: 2001
To Be Retired: Dec. 2001
Original Price: $17.50
Value by Year Mark:
I–$17.50 **II**–$17.50

9 #726737

**Trudy
(Abbey Press Early Release, also sold as set w/plush piece)**
"Bearing Easter Blessings"
Issued: 2000 • Closed: 2000
Original Price: $19.95
Value by Year Mark: **9**–$50 **I**–$42

10 #127973

Tucker & Travis
"We're In This Together"
Issued: 1995 • Current
Original Price: $25
Value by Year Mark:
4–$52 **5**–$42 **6**–$35 **7**–$29
8–$28 **9**–$25 **I**–$25 **II**–$25

Figurines

	Price Paid	Value
1.		
2.		
3.		
4.		
5.		
6.		
7.		
8.		
9.		
10.		

Totals

Figurines

1 #738638

Val (Limited Edition, sold as set w/watch)
"It's Always Time To Say I Love You"
Issued: 2000 • Closed: 2000
Original Price: $30
Value by Year Mark: 9–$40 I–$40

2 #916382 **3**

Valentine Mini Figurine (3 asst.)
"Hugs & Kisses"
Issued: 1994
Out Of Production: 1998
Original Price: $7
Value: $15

3 #916382

Valentine Mini Figurine (3 asst.)
"Love Ya"
Issued: 1994
Out Of Production: 1998
Original Price: $7
Value: $15

4 #916382

Valentine Mini Figurine (3 asst.)
"You're Purr-fect"
Issued: 1994
Out Of Production: 1998
Original Price: $7
Value: $15

5 #366854

Veronica (1998 Catalog Exclusive)
"You Make Happiness Bloom"
Issued: 1998 • Closed: 1998
Original Price: $15
Value by Year Mark: 8–$42
Variation: International Exclusive, #366854I
Value: $46

6 #916293

Victoria
"From My Heart To Yours"
Issued: 1994 • Suspended: 1995
Original Price: $16.50
Value by Year Mark:
3–$92 4–$84 5–$68

Figurines

	Price Paid	Value
1.		
2.		
3.	7⁰⁰	15⁰⁰
4.		
5.		
6.		
7.		
8.		
9.		
10.		
Totals		

7 #156280

Violet
"Blessings Bloom When You Are Near"
Issued: 1996 • Retired: 1999
Original Price: $15
Value by Year Mark:
5–$39 6–$30 7–$25
8–$22 9–$19

8 #786705
New

Wanda
"A Sprinkling Of Fairy Dust Will Make You Feel Better"
Issued: 2001 • Current
Original Price: $20
Value by Year Mark: I–$20 II–$20

9 #848565
New

Wendall (LE-2001)
"Have You Been Naughty Or Nice?"
Issued: 2001
To Be Retired: 2001
Original Price: $25
Value by Year Mark: I–$25 II–$25

10 #476846

Wesley, Philip, Fiona and Renee (1999 Collectible Exposition Figurine)
"The Company We Keep Is A Reflection Of Ourselves"
Issued: 1999 • Closed: 1999
Original Price: $30
Value by Year Mark: 9–$100

Figurines

1 New #706949

"Whatever The Distance, A Friend Stays With You"
Issued: 2001 • Current
Original Price: $17.50
Value by Year Mark:
I–$17.50 II–$17.50

2 New #770469

When I Need A Hug, I Run To Dad!
Issued: 2001 • Current
Original Price: $15
Value by Year Mark: I–$15 II–$15

3 #302678

Whitney
"We Make A Winning Team"
Issued: 1998 • Current
Original Price: $15
Value by Year Mark:
7–$25 8–$20 9–$15 I–$15 II–$15

4 #617164

Willie
"Bears Of A Feather Stay Together"
Issued: 1994 • Retired: 1997
Original Price: $15
Value by Year Mark:
4–$55 5–$46 6–$36

5 #476811

Winfield (Special Millennium Limited Edition)
"Anything Is Possible When You Wish On A Star"
Issued: 1999 • Current
Original Price: $50
Value by Year Mark:
8–$60 9–$50 I–$50 II–$50

6 #617172

Winona
"Little Fair Feather Friend"
Issued: 1994 • Retired: 1997
Original Price: $15
Value by Year Mark:
4–$52 5–$47 6–$37

7 #629707

Wyatt
"I'm Called Little Running Bear"
Issued: 1994 • Retired: 1998
Original Price: $15
Value by Year Mark:
4–$44 5–$36 6–$29
7–$25 8–$22

8 #617121

Wylie
"I'm Called Little Friend"
Issued: 1994 • Retired: 1998
Original Price: $15
Value by Year Mark:
4–$44 5–$32 6–$27
7–$22 8–$22

9 #215880

"You Grow More Dear With Each Passing Year"
Issued: 1997 • Current
Original Price: $25
Value by Year Mark:
7–$28 8–$25 9–$25 I–$25 II–$25

10 #306398

"You're The Frosting On The Birthday Cake"
Issued: 1998 • Current
Original Price: $22.50
Value by Year Mark:
7–$29 8–$22.50
9–$22.50 I–$22.50 II–$22.50

Figurines

	Price Paid	Value
1.	17⁵⁰	17⁵⁰
2.		
3.		
4.		
5.		
6.		
7.		
8.		
9.		
10.		
Totals		

Figurines

1 #302759

"You're The Key To My Heart" Mini Figurine (2 asst.)
Issued: 1998 • Current
Original Price: $7.50
Value: $7.50

2 #302759

"You're The Key To My Heart Mini Figurine" (2 asst.)
Issued: 1998 • Current
Original Price: $7.50
Value: $7.50

3 #950491

Zachary
*"Yesterday's Memories
Are Today's Treasures"*
Issued: 1992 • Retired: 1997
Original Price: $30
Value by Year Mark:
LETTER–$75 **3**–$62
4–$50 **5**–$47 **6**–$41

Figurines

	Price Paid	Value
1.		
2.		
3.		
Totals		

Series

New series join the **Cherished Teddies** family each year, each one "bearing" (no pun intended, well, maybe a little bit of one) a special theme of its own. This past year, the teddies have had lifelong friendships with the *Friends To The End* series and show off their sensitive side with *Heart Strings* – just to name a few!

1   #276995   **2**   #276995P

ACROSS THE SEAS

Bazza (Australia)
"I'm Lost Down Under Without You"
Issued: 1997 • Retired: 1999
Original Price: $17.50
Value by Year Mark:
7–$26 **8**–$22 **9**–$20

Bazza (International Exclusive, sold w/passport)
"'m Lost Down Under Without You"
Issued: 1996 • Retired: 1999
Original Price: N/A
Value: $30

③   #202444P   **4**   #202339

Bob (United States, sold w/passport)
"Our Friendship Is From Sea To Shining Sea"
Issued: 1996 • Retired: 1999
Original Price: $17.50
Value by Year Mark:
6–$30 **7**–$22 **8**–$20 **9**–$20

Carlos (Mexico)
"I Found An Amigo In You"
Issued: 1996 • Retired: 1999
Original Price: $17.50
Value by Year Mark:
6–$30 **7**–$25 **8**–$22 **9**–$20

5   #197254   **6**   #373966

Claudette (France)
"Our Friendship Is Bon Appetit!"
Issued: 1996 • Retired: 1999
Original Price: $17.50
Value by Year Mark:
6–$29 **7**–$20 **8**–$20 **9**–$20

Colleen (Ireland)
"The Luck Of The Irish To You"
Issued: 1998 • Retired: 1999
Original Price: $17.50
Value by Year Mark:
8–$55 **9**–$35

Across The Seas

	Price Paid	Value
1.		
2.		
3.	17.50	30.00
4.		
5.		
6.		
Totals		

Across The Seas

1.

#202355

Fernando (Spain)
"You Make Everyday A Fiesta"
Issued: 1996 • Retired: 1999
Original Price: $17.50
Value by Year Mark:
6–$29 7–$20 8–$20 9–$20

2.

#202436

Franz (Germany)
*"Our Friendship Knows
No Boundaries"*
Issued: 1996 • Retired: 1999
Original Price: $17.50
Value by Year Mark:
6–$30 7–$26 8–$20 9–$20

3.

#202436P

**Franz
(International Exclusive,
sold w/passport)**
*"Our Friendship Knows
No Boundaries"*
Issued: 1996 • Retired: 1999
Original Price: N/A
Value: $30

4.

#202401

Katrien (Holland)
"Tulips Blossom With Friendship"
Issued: 1996 • Retired: 1999
Original Price: $17.50
Value by Year Mark:
6–$29 7–$20 8–$20 9–$20
Variation: "Cherished" missing
on bottom
Value by Year Mark: 6–$43

5.

#202401P

**Katrien
(International Exclusive,
sold w/passport)**
"Tulips Blossom With Friendship"
Issued: 1996 • Retired: 1999
Original Price: N/A
Value: N/E

6.

#197289

Kerstin (Sweden)
"You're The Swedish Of Them All"
Issued: 1996 • Retired: 1999
Original Price: $17.50
Value by Year Mark:
6–$29 7–$20 8–$20 9–$20

7.

#302627

Leilani (Tahiti)
*"Sending You Warm And
Friendly Island Breezes"*
Issued: 1998 • Retired: 1998
Original Price: $17.50
Value: 8–$50

8.

#202347

Lian (China)
*"Our Friendship Spans
Many Miles"*
Issued: 1996 • Retired: 1998
Original Price: $17.50
Value by Year Mark:
6–$38 7–$30 8–$25

9.

#202452

Lorna (Scotland)
"Our Love Is In The Highlands"
Issued: 1996 • Retired: 1999
Original Price: $17.50
Value by Year Mark:
6–$29 7–$20 8–$20 9–$20

10.

#202452P

**Lorna
(International Exclusive,
sold w/passport)**
"Our Love Is In The Highlands"
Issued: 1996 • Retired: 1999
Original Price: N/A
Value: N/E

Across The Seas

	Price Paid	Value
1.	17⁵⁰	29⁰⁰
2.		
3.		
4.		
5.		
6.		
7.		
8.	17⁵⁰	38⁰⁰
9.		
10.		
Totals		

1 #202312

Machiko (Japan)
*"Love Fans A Beautiful
Friendship"*
Issued: 1996 • Retired: 1998
Original Price: $17.50
Value by Year Mark:
6–$35 7–$28 8–$24

2 #202320

Nadia (Russia)
"From Russia, With Love"
Issued: 1996 • Retired: 1999
Original Price: $17.50
Value by Year Mark:
6–$30 7–$25 8–$22 9–$20

3 #216739

Preston (Canada)
*"Riding Across The Great
White North"*
Issued: 1996 • Retired: 1998
Original Price: $17.50
Value by Year Mark:
6–$32 7–$27 8–$24

4 #216739P

**Preston
(International Exclusive,
sold w/passport)**
*"Riding Across The Great
White North"*
Issued: 1996 • Retired: 1998
Original Price: N/A
Value: N/E

5 #202398

Rajul (India)
"You're The Jewel Of My Heart"
Issued: 1996 • Retired: 1999
Original Price: $17.50
Value by Year Mark:
6–$28 7–$24 8–$20 9–$20

6 #276987

Sophia (Italy)
*"Like Grapes On The Vine, Our
Friendship Is Divine"*
Issued: 1997 • Retired: 1999
Original Price: $17.50
Value by Year Mark:
7–$28 8–$22 9–$20

7 #202878

William (England)
"You're A Jolly Ol' Chap!"
Issued: 1996 • Retired: 1999
Original Price: $17.50
Value by Year Mark:
6–$32 7–$27 8–$23 9–$20

8 #202878P

**William
(International Exclusive,
sold w/passport)**
"You're A Jolly Ol' Chap!"
Issued: 1996 • Retired: 1999
Original Price: N/A
Value: N/E

AMERICAN
CLASSICS

9 #811742

New

Jerald And Mary Ann
*"What Would Game Night
Be Without You?"*
Issued: 2001 • Current
Original Price: $27.50
Value by Year Mark:
I–$27.50 II–$27.50

Across The Seas

	Price Paid	Value
1.		
2.		
3.		
4.		
5.		
6.		
7.		
8.		

American Classics

9.		

Totals

ANGELS

1 #175986

Angela (LE-1998)
"Peace On Earth And Mercy Mild"
Issued: 1998 • Closed: 1998
Original Price: $20
Value by Year Mark: 8–$42

2 #175994

Grace (LE-1997)
"Glory To The Newborn King"
Issued: 1997 • Closed: 1997
Original Price: $20
Value by Year Mark: 7–$40

3 #176001

Stormi (LE-1996)
"Hark The Herald Angels Sing"
Issued: 1996 • Closed: 1996
Original Price: $20
Value by Year Mark: 6–$56

ANTIQUE TOYS

4 #537217

"A Big Hug From A Little Friend"
Issued: 1999
Out Of Production: 2000
Original Price: $12.50
Value: N/E

5 #537187

"Everyone Needs An Occasional Hug"
Issued: 1999
Out Of Production: 2000
Original Price: $12.50
Value: N/E

6 #537241

"Follow Your Heart Wherever It Takes You"
Issued: 1999
Out Of Production: 2000
Original Price: $12.50
Value: N/E

7 #537233

"A Friend Is An Answered Prayer"
Issued: 1999
Out Of Production: 2000
Original Price: $12.50
Value: N/E

8 #537268

"A Journey With You Is One To Remember"
Issued: 1999
Out Of Production: 2000
Original Price: $12.50
Value: N/E

Angels

	Price Paid	Value
1.		
2.		
3.		

Antique Toys

4.		
5.		
6.		
7.		
8.		

Totals

1 #537195

"Keep Good Friends Close To Your Heart"
Issued: 1999
Out Of Production: 2000
Original Price: $12.50
Value: N/E

2 #537209

"Our Friendship Is An Adventure"
Issued: 1999
Out Of Production: 2000
Original Price: $12.50
Value: N/E

3 #537225

"You Have The Biggest Heart Of All"
Issued: 1999
Out Of Production: 2000
Original Price: $12.50
Value: N/E

BEAR BUSINESS

4 #476528

Anthony
"Friendship Is A Work Of Art"
Issued: 2000 • Current
Original Price: $20
Value by Year Mark:
9–$22 I–$22 II–$20

5 #476528R

Anthony (Rare Bear)
"Friendship Is A Work Of Art"
Issued: 2000 • Current
Original Price: $20
Value by Year Mark:
9–$50 I–$35 II–$20

6 #676942

Corey
"I Know How To Take Care Of Business"
Issued: 2000 • Current
Original Price: $22.50
Value by Year Mark:
9–$22.50 I–$22.50 II–$22.50

7 #476587

Harriet
"You Make Me Feel Beautiful Inside"
Issued: 2000 • Current
Original Price: $22.50
Value by Year Mark:
9–$22.50 I–$22.50 II–$22.50

8 #476560

Kent
"Officer, I've Got A Warrant Out For Your Heart"
Issued: 2000 • Current
Original Price: $20
Value by Year Mark:
9–$20 I–$20 II–$20

9 #476560R

Kent (Rare Bear)
"Officer, I've Got A Warrant Out For Your Heart"
Issued: 2000 • Current
Original Price: $20
Value by Year Mark:
9–$45 I–$35 II–$20

Antique Toys/Bear Business

Antique Toys

	Price Paid	Value
1.		
2.		
3.		

Bear Business

4.		
5.		
6.		
7.		
8.		
9.		
Totals		

Bear Business/Beta Is For Bears

1 #476544

Woody
"You Hold Everything In Place"
Issued: 2000 • Current
Original Price: $20
Value by Year Mark: I–$20 II–$20

BETA IS FOR BEARS

2 #305995

Greek Alpha Bear
Issued: 1998 • Current
Original Price: $7.50
Value: $7.50

3 #306002

Greek Beta Bear
Issued: 1998 • Current
Original Price: $7.50
Value: $7.50

4 #306010

Greek Gamma Bear
Issued: 1998 • Current
Original Price: $7.50
Value: $7.50

5 #306037

Greek Delta Bear
Issued: 1998 • Current
Original Price: $7.50
Value: $7.50

6 #306045

Greek Epsilon Bear
Issued: 1998 • Current
Original Price: $7.50
Value: $7.50

7 #306053

Greek Zeta Bear
Issued: 1998 • Current
Original Price: $7.50
Value: $7.50

8 #306088

Greek Eta Bear
Issued: 1998 • Current
Original Price: $7.50
Value: $7.50

9 #306096

Greek Theta Bear
Issued: 1998 • Current
Original Price: $7.50
Value: $7.50

Bear Business

	Price Paid	Value
1.		

Beta Is For Bears

2.		
3.		
4.		
5.		
6.		
7.		
8.		
9.		

Totals

1 #306118

Greek Iota Bear
Issued: 1998 • Current
Original Price: $7.50
Value: $7.50

2 #306126

Greek Kappa Bear
Issued: 1998 • Current
Original Price: $7.50
Value: $7.50

3 #306134

Greek Lambda Bear
Issued: 1998 • Current
Original Price: $7.50
Value: $7.50

4 #306142

Greek Mu Bear
Issued: 1998 • Current
Original Price: $7.50
Value: $7.50

5 #306150

Greek Nu Bear
Issued: 1998 • Current
Original Price: $7.50
Value: $7.50

6 #306185

Greek Xi Bear
Issued: 1998 • Current
Original Price: $7.50
Value: $7.50

7 #306193

Greek Omicron Bear
Issued: 1998 • Current
Original Price: $7.50
Value: $7.50

8 #306207

Greek Pi Bear
Issued: 1998 • Current
Original Price: $7.50
Value: $7.50

9 #306215

Greek Rho Bear
Issued: 1998 • Current
Original Price: $7.50
Value: $7.50

10 #306223

Greek Sigma Bear
Issued: 1998 • Current
Original Price: $7.50
Value: $7.50

Beta Is For Bears

	Price Paid	Value
1.		
2.		
3.		
4.		
5.		
6.		
7.		
8.		
9.		
10.		
Totals		

Beta Is For Bears/Blossoms Of Friendship

1 #306231

Greek Tau Bear
Issued: 1998 • Current
Original Price: $7.50
Value: $7.50

2 #306258

Greek Upsilon Bear
Issued: 1998 • Current
Original Price: $7.50
Value: $7.50

3 #306266

Greek Phi Bear
Issued: 1998 • Current
Original Price: $7.50
Value: $7.50

4 #306274

Greek Chi Bear
Issued: 1998 • Current
Original Price: $7.50
Value: $7.50

5 #306282

Greek Psi Bear
Issued: 1998 • Current
Original Price: $7.50
Value: $7.50

6 #306290

Greek Omega Bear
Issued: 1998 • Current
Original Price: $7.50
Value: $7.50

Beta Is For Bears

	Price Paid	Value
1.		
2.		
3.		
4.		
5.		
6.		

Blossoms Of Friendship

7.		
8.		
9.		

Totals

BLOSSOMS OF FRIENDSHIP

7 #202932

Dahlia
*"You're The Best Pick
Of The Bunch"*
Issued: 1997 • Retired: 2000
Original Price: $15
Value by Year Mark:
6–$25 7–$18 8–$17 9–$17 I–$17

8 #202908

Iris
"You're The Iris Of My Eye"
Issued: 1997 • Retired: 2000
Original Price: $15
Value by Year Mark:
6–$25 7–$18 8–$17 9–$17 I–$17

9 #202959

Lily
*"Lilies Bloom With
Petals Of Hope"*
Issued: 1998 • Retired: 2000
Original Price: $15
Value by Year Mark:
8–$19 9–$17 I–$17

1 #202959A

Lily
(1997 Catalog Exclusive)
"Lilies Bloom With
Petals Of Hope"
Issued: 1997 • Closed: 1997
Original Price: $15
Value by Year Mark: 6–$38 7–N/E

2 #202967

Ornamental Furniture
Figurines (set/3)
Issued: 1997 • Current
Original Price: $17.50
Value: $17.50

3 #202886

Rose
"Everything's Coming Up Roses"
Issued: 1997 • Retired: 2000
Original Price: $15
Value by Year Mark:
6–$27 7–$20 8–$17 9–$17 I–$17

4 #202894

Susan
"Love Stems From
Our Friendship"
Issued: 1997 • Retired: 2000
Original Price: $15
Value by Year Mark:
6–$29 7–$20 8–$19 9–$17 I–$17

BONNETS AND
BOWS

5 #662518

Collette
"Outer Beauty Is A Reflection
Of Inner Beauty"
Issued: 2000 • Current
Original Price: $20
Value by Year Mark:
9–$20 I–$20 II–$20

6 #662461

Theresa
"You Have Such
Wonderful Grace"
Issued: 2000 • Current
Original Price: $20
Value by Year Mark:
9–$20 I–$20 II–$20

7 #662437

Vanessa
"You're My Shelter From
The Storm"
Issued: 2000 • Current
Original Price: $22.50
Value by Year Mark:
9–$22.50 I–$22.50 II–$22.50

8 #662496

Wilfred
"A Lifetime Of Friendship . . .
A Trunk Full Of Memories"
Issued: 2000 • Current
Original Price: $25
Value by Year Mark:
9–$25 I–$25 II–$25

BY THE SEA,
BY THE SEA

Blossoms Of Friendship

	Price Paid	Value
1.		
2.		
3.		
4.		

Bonnets And Bows

5.		
6.		
7.		
8.		
Totals		

By The Sea, By The Sea/Carousel

1 #203505 **2** #203475 **3** #203513

Gregg
"Everything Pails In Comparison To Friends"
Issued: 1997 • Retired: 2000
Original Price: $20
Value by Year Mark: 6–$30 7–$26
8–$22 9–$22 I–$22

Jerry
"Ready To Make A Splash"
Issued: 1997 • Retired: 2000
Original Price: $17.50
Value by Year Mark: 6–$28 7–$23
8–$19 9–$19 I–$19

Jim And Joey
"Underneath It All We're Forever Friends"
Issued: 1997 • Retired: 2000
Original Price: $25
Value by Year Mark: 6–$36 7–$30
8–$27 9–$27 I–$27

4 #203491 **5** #203467

CAROUSEL

Judy
"I'm Your Bathing Beauty"
Issued: 1997 • Retired: 2000
Original Price: $35
Value by Year Mark: 6–$46 7–$40
8–$37 9–$37 I–$37

Sandy
"There's Room In My Sand Castle For You"
Issued: 1997 • Retired: 2000
Original Price: $20
Value by Year Mark: 6–$31 7–$26
8–$24 9–$22 I–$22

By The Sea, By The Sea

	Price Paid	Value
1.		
2.	8.75	28⁰⁰
3.	25⁰⁰	36⁰⁰
4.		
5.		

Carousel

6.		
7.		
8.		
9.		

Totals

6 #589977 **7** #505552

Archie
"Through Ups And Downs, You're Still The Best Friend Around"
Issued: 1999 • Current
Original Price: $20
Value by Year Mark:
8–$22 9–$20 I–$20 II–$20

Bill
"Friends Like You Are Always True Blue"
Issued: 1999 • Retired: 2000
Original Price: $20
Value by Year Mark:
8–$24 9–$22 I–$22

8 #505498 **9** #589942

Cody
"I'll Cherish You For Many Moons"
Issued: 1999 • Retired: 2000
Original Price: $20
Value by Year Mark:
8–$24 9–$22 I–$22

Crystal
"Hang On! We're In For A Wonderful Ride"
Issued: 1999 • Current
Original Price: $20
Value by Year Mark:
8–$22 9–$20 I–$20 II–$20

1 #589942R

Crystal (Rare Bear)
*"Hang On! We're In For
A Wonderful Ride"*
Issued: 1999 • Closed: 1999
Original Price: $20
Value: $50

2 #589950

Flossie
*"I'd Stick My Neck Out
For You Anytime"*
Issued: 1999 • Current
Original Price: $20
Value by Year Mark:
8–$22 9–$20 I–$20 II–$20

3 #502898

Gina
*"Where Friends Gather,
Magic Blossoms"*
Issued: 1999 • Retired: 2000
Original Price: $20
Value by Year Mark:
8–$24 9–$22 I–$22

4 #589969

Ivan
*"I've Packed My Trunk And
I'm Ready To Go"*
Issued: 1999 • Current
Original Price: $20
Value by Year Mark:
8–$22 9–$20 I–$20 II–$20

5 #506214

Jason
*"When It Comes To Friendship,
You've Really Earned
Your Stripes"*
Issued: 1999 • Retired: 2000
Original Price: $20
Value by Year Mark:
8–$24 9–$22 I–$22

6 #505579

Jenelle
*"A Friend Is Somebunny To
Cherish Forever"*
Issued: 1999 • Retired: 2000
Original Price: $20
Value by Year Mark:
8–$24 9–$22 I–$22

7 #589926

Jerrod
*"Don't Worry – It's Just Another
Little Bump In The Road"*
Issued: 1999 • Current
Original Price: $20
Value by Year Mark:
8–$22 9–$20 I–$20 II–$20

8 #589934

Marcus
*"There's Nobody I'd Rather Go
'Round With Than You"*
Issued: 1999 • Current
Original Price: $20
Value by Year Mark:
8–$22 9–$20 I–$20 II–$20

9 #506206

Virginia
*"It's So Merry Going
'Round With You"*
Issued: 1999 • Retired: 2000
Original Price: $20
Value by Year Mark:
8–$24 9–$22 I–$22

**CAROUSEL
BIRTHSTONES
(AVON
EXCLUSIVES)**

Carousel

	Price Paid	Value
1.		
2.		
3.		
4.		
5.		
6.		
7.		
8.		
9.		
Totals		

Carousel Birthstones

1 N/A

January (garnet)
Issued: 2000 • Closed: 2000
Original Price: $12.99
Value by Year Mark: ▮—$18

2 N/A

February (amethyst)
Issued: 2000 • Closed: 2000
Original Price: $12.99
Value by Year Mark: ▮—$18

3 N/A

March (aquamarine)
Issued: 2000 • Closed: 2000
Original Price: $12.99
Value by Year Mark: ▮—$18

4 N/A

April (diamond)
Issued: 2000 • Closed: 2000
Original Price: $12.99
Value by Year Mark: ▮—$18

5 N/A

May (emerald)
Issued: 2000 • Closed: 2000
Original Price: $12.99
Value by Year Mark: ▮—$18

6 N/A

June (alexandrite)
Issued: 2000 • Closed: 2000
Original Price: $12.99
Value by Year Mark: ▮—$18

7 N/A

July (ruby)
Issued: 2000 • Closed: 2000
Original Price: $12.99
Value by Year Mark: ▮—$18

8 N/A

August (peridot)
Issued: 2000 • Closed: 2000
Original Price: $12.99
Value by Year Mark: ▮—$18

9 N/A

September (sapphire)
Issued: 2000 • Closed: 2000
Original Price: $12.99
Value by Year Mark: ▮—$18

10 N/A

October (rose zircon)
Issued: 2000 • Closed: 2000
Original Price: $12.99
Value by Year Mark: ▮—$18

Carousel Birthstones (Avon Exclusives)		
	Price Paid	Value
1.		
2.		
3.		
4.		
5.		
6.		
7.		
8.		
9.		
10.		
Totals		

1 N/A

November (topaz)
Issued: 2000 • Closed: 2000
Original Price: $12.99
Value by Year Mark: I—$18

2 N/A

December (blue zircon)
Issued: 2000 • Closed: 2000
Original Price: $12.99
Value by Year Mark: I—$18

**CHERISHED
SNOWBEARS**

3 #706892

Buddy
"And The North Wind Shall Blow"
Issued: 2000 • Current
Original Price: $25
Value by Year Mark: I—$25 II—$25

4 #848573

New

Delight
"I Will Melt Your Heart"
Issued: 2001 • Current
Original Price: $25
Value by Year Mark: I—$25 II—$25

5 #865036

New

Erika (Dated 2001)
*"Remember The Past, Cherish
The Years Ahead"*
Issued: 2001 • To Be Retired: 2001
Original Price: $25
Value by Year Mark: I—$25 II—$25

6 #706906

New

Merry
*"In The Meadow We Can
Build A Snowman"*
Issued: 2000 • Current
Original Price: $25
Value by Year Mark: I—$25 II—$25

7 #848581

New

Nora
"Brrrrr . . . "
Issued: 2001 • Current
Original Price: $25
Value by Year Mark: I—$25 II—$25

8 #848603

New

Ursula & Bernhard
*"In The Winter, We Can
Build A Snowman"*
Issued: 2001 • Current
Original Price: $30
Value by Year Mark: I—$30 II—$30

**CHERISHED
TEDDIES AND
FRIENDS**

Carousel Birthstones (Avon Exclusives)		
	Price Paid	Value
1.		
2.		

Cherished Snowbears	
3.	
4.	
5.	
6.	
7.	
8.	
Totals	

Carousel/Cherished/Cherished

Cherished Teddies And Friends

1 #662011

Bailey And Friend
"The Only Thing More Contagious Than A Cold Is A Best Friend"
Issued: 2000 • Current
Original Price: $22.50
Value by Year Mark:
9–$22.50 I–$22.50 II–$22.50
Variation: Initial Production Run, #662011F
Value: N/E

2 #644358

Baxter
"It's Not The Size Of The Friend, But The Size Of Their Heart"
Issued: 2000 • Current
Original Price: $22.50
Value by Year Mark:
9–$22.50 I–$22.50 II–$22.50
Variation: Initial Production Run, #644358F
Value: N/E

3 #661996

Caleb And Friends (Limited Edition)
"When One Lacks Vision, Another Must Provide Supervision"
Issued: 2000 • Retired: 2000
Original Price: N/A
Value by Year Mark: 9–N/E I–N/E

4 #706817

Carter And Friends (Special Issue)
"Take Time For Others And Others Will Take Time For You"
Issued: 2000 • Current
Original Price: $25
Value by Year Mark:
9–$25 I–$25 II–$25

5 #786691

Elmer And Friends
"Friends Are The Thread That Holds The Quilt Of The Life Together"
Issued: 2000 • Current
Original Price: $30
Value by Year Mark: I–$30 II–$30

6 #662038

Heather And Friends (Toys For Tots Exclusive, sold as set w/plush piece)
"Remembering The Simple Pleasures Of Childhood"
Issued: 2000 • Current
Original Price: $37.50
Value by Year Mark:
9–$37.50 I–$37.50 II–$37.50

7 #662046

Homer And Friends
"Adventure Is Just Around The Corner"
Issued: 2000 • Current
Original Price: $35
Value by Year Mark:
9–$35 I–$35 II–$35
Variation: Initial Production Run, #662046F
Value: N/E

8 #662003

Sawyer And Friends
"Hold On To The Past, But Look To The Future"
Issued: 2000 • Current
Original Price: $27.50
Value by Year Mark:
9–$27.50 I–$27.50 II–$27.50
Variation: Initial Production Run, #662003F
Value: N/E

9 #661953

Tess And Friend
"Things Do Not Change, We Do"
Issued: 2000 • Current
Original Price: $27.50
Value by Year Mark:
9–$27.50 I–$27.50 II–$27.50
Variation: Initial Production Run, #661933F
Value: N/E

10 #786683

Todd And Friend
"Share Life's Little Joys With Your Closest Friend"
Issued: 2000 • Current
Original Price: $25
Value by Year Mark: I–$25 II–$25

Cherished Teddies And Friends

	Price Paid	Value
1.		
2.		
3.		
4.		
5.		
6.		
7.		
8.		
9.		
10.		
Totals		

Cherished Teddies Quilts (Direct Mail Exclusive)

1   #741094

Photo Unavailable

"I'm A Beary Lucky Groom"
Issued: 2000 • Current
Original Price: N/A
Value by Year Mark: I–N/A II–N/A

2   #741094

"You Have Taught Me What It Means To Be A Friend"
Issued: 2000 • Current
Original Price: N/A
Value by Year Mark: I–N/A II–N/A

Childhood Memories

3   #661848

Albert And Susann
"Whenever Life Hands You Lemons, Make Lemonade"
Issued: 2000 • Current
Original Price: $30
Value by Year Mark:
9–$30 I–$30 II–$30
Variation: Early Edition, #661848S
Value by Year Mark: 9–$40 I–$35

4   #706965

New

Calvin
"Life Is Filled With Ups And Downs"
Issued: 2001 • Current
Original Price: $17.50
Value by Year Mark:
I–$17.50 II–$17.50

5   #706744

Clement And Jodie
"Try, Try And Try Again!"
Issued: 2000 • Current
Original Price: $20
Value by Year Mark: I–$20 II–$20

6   #661791

Dad, Drake And Dustee
"You Have A Very Special Way Of Lifting Spirits"
Issued: 2000 • Current
Original Price: $25
Value by Year Mark: I–$25 II–$25

7   #661899

Dawn
"Every Once In A While, There's A Bump In The Road"
Issued: 2000 • Current
Original Price: $17.50
Value by Year Mark:
9–$17.50 I–$17.50 II–$17.50

8   #661864

Ernest and Bugsy
"Looks Like Trouble Is Just Around The Corner"
Issued: 2000 • Current
Original Price: $25
Value by Year Mark:
9–$25 I–$25 II–$25

Cherished Teddies Quilts

	Price Paid	Value
1.		
2.		

Childhood Memories

3.		
4.		
5.		
6.		
7.		
8.		

Totals

Childhood Memories/Circus

1 #661856

Fred
*"You're The Best Thing
Since Sliced Bread"*
Issued: 2000 • Current
Original Price: $27.50
Value by Year Mark:
9–$27.50 I–$27.50 II–$27.50

2 #661872

Kim
*"Treat Yourself To Life's
Little Pleasures"*
Issued: 2000 • Current
Original Price: $17.50
Value by Year Mark:
I–$17.50 II–$17.50

3 #661880

Lorraine
"Don't Let It Get You Down"
Issued: 2000 • Current
Original Price: $17.50
Value by Year Mark:
I–$17.50 II–$17.50

4 #661821

Melinda
*"I'm Only A Hop, Skip And A
Jump Away If You Need Me"*
Issued: 2000 • Current
Original Price: $17.50
Value by Year Mark:
I–$17.50 II–$17.50

5 #661783

Russell And Ross
*"Thanks For Teaching Me
About The Real World"*
Issued: 2000 • Current
Original Price: $22.50
Value by Year Mark:
I–$22.50 II–$22.50

CIRCUS

Childhood Memories

	Price Paid	Value
1.		
2.		
3.		
4.		
5.		

Circus

6.		
7.		
8.		

Totals

6 #103713

Bruno
"Step Right Up And Smile"
Issued: 1996 • Retired: 2000
Original Price: $17.50
Value by Year Mark: 5–$34 6–$27
7–$22 8–$19 9–$19 I–$19

7 #103977

**Circus Elephant
With Bear**
"Trunk Full Of Bear Hugs"
Issued: 1996 • Retired: 2000
Original Price: $22.50
Value by Year Mark: 5–$35 6–$30
7–$27 8–$24 9–$24 I–$24

8 #104256

*Circus
Tent With
Rings*

Claudia

Bruno

Wally

Circus Gift Set (set/5)
Issued: 1996 • Retired: 2000
Original Price: $75
Value by Year Mark: 5–$121 6–$100 7–$85 8–$78 9–$78 I–$78

1 #203548

Circus Lion
"You're My Mane Attraction"
Issued: 1997 • Retired: 2000
Original Price: $12.50
Value by Year Mark: 6–$21 7–$16
8–$15 9–$15 I–$15

2 #137596

Circus Seal With Ball
"Seal Of Friendship"
Issued: 1996 • Retired: 2000
Original Price: $10
Value by Year Mark: 5–$24 6–$15
7–$12 8–$12 9–$12 I–$12

3 #107700

Circus Tent With Rings (set/2)
Issued: 1996 • Current
Original Price: $22.50
Value: $22.50

4 #103721

Claudia
"You Take The Center Ring With Me"
Issued: 1996 • Retired: 2000
Original Price: $17.50
Value by Year Mark: 5–$34 6–$27
7–$22 8–$19 9–$19 I–$19

5 #111430

Clown On Ball (musical)
♪ *"Put On A Happy Face"*
Issued: 1996 • Current
Original Price: $40
Value: $40

6 #103748

Dudley
"Just Clowning Around"
Issued: 1997 • Retired: 2000
Original Price: $17.50
Value by Year Mark: 6–$25 7–$22
8–$19 9–$19 I–$19

7 #103756

Logan
"Love Is A Bear Necessity"
Issued: 1997 • Retired: 2000
Original Price: $17.50
Value by Year Mark: 6–$29 7–$22
8–$19 9–$19 I–$19
Variation: "Limited To Year Of Production" on understamp
Value: $48

8 #203572

Shelby
"Friendship Keeps You Popping"
Issued: 1997 • Retired: 2000
Original Price: $17.50
Value by Year Mark: 6–$25 7–$22
8–$19 9–$19 I–$19

9 #103942

Tonya (set/2)
"Friends Are Bear Essentials"
Issued: 1997 • Retired: 2000
Original Price: $20
Value by Year Mark: 6–$30 7–$25
8–$22 9–$22 I–$22

10 #103934

Wally
"You're The Tops With Me"
Issued: 1996 • Retired: 2000
Original Price: $17.50
Value by Year Mark: 5–$33 6–$27
7–$22 8–$19 9–$19 I–$19

Circus

	Price Paid	Value
1.		
2.		
3.		
4.		
5.		
6.		
7.		
8.		
9.		
10.		
Totals		

CoCa-Cola®

COUNT ON ME

1 #707007

New

Dewey
*"Enjoy Your Friends, They're
The Refreshments Of Life"*
Issued: 2001 • Current
Original Price: $25
Value by Year Mark:
I–$25   II– $25

2 #302945

Bear With 0 Block
Issued: 1998 • Current
Original Price: $5
Value: $5

3 #302821

Bear With 1 Block
Issued: 1998 • Current
Original Price: $5
Value: $5

4 #302848

Bear With 2 Block
Issued: 1998 • Current
Original Price: $5
Value: $5

5 #302856

Bear With 3 Block
Issued: 1998 • Current
Original Price: $5
Value: $5

6 #302864

Bear With 4 Block
Issued: 1998 • Current
Original Price: $5
Value: $5

7 #302872

Bear With 5 Block
Issued: 1998 • Current
Original Price: $5
Value: $5

8 #302899

Bear With 6 Block
Issued: 1998 • Current
Original Price: $5
Value: $5

Coca-Cola®		
	Price Paid	Value
1.		

Count On Me		
2.		
3.		
4.		
5.		
6.		
7.		
8.		
Totals		

1   #302902

Bear With 7 Block
Issued: 1998 • Current
Original Price: $5
Value: $5

2   #302910

Bear With 8 Block
Issued: 1998 • Current
Original Price: $5
Value: $5

3   #302929

Bear With 9 Block
Issued: 1998 • Current
Original Price: $5
Value: $5

Days Of The Week

4   #789720
New

Frances
*"Friday's Child Is Loving
And Giving"*
Issued: 2001 • Current
Original Price: $20
Value by Year Mark: I–$20 II–$20

5   #789682
New

Monica
"Monday's Child Is Fair Of Face"
Issued: 2001 • Current
Original Price: $20
Value by Year Mark: I–$20 II–$20

6   #789739
New

Sandra
*"Saturday's Child Works
Hard For A Living"*
Issued: 2001 • Current
Original Price: $20
Value by Year Mark: I–$20 II–$20

7   #789674
New

Sunny
*"The Child That Is Born On The
Sabbath Day Is Bonny And
Blithe And Gay"*
Issued: 2001 • Current
Original Price: $20
Value by Year Mark: I–$20 II–$20

8   #789712
New

Thelma
"Thursday's Child Has Far To Go"
Issued: 2001 • Current
Original Price: $20
Value by Year Mark: I–$20 II–$20

9   #789690
New

Tia
"Tuesday's Child Is Full Of Grace"
Issued: 2001 • Current
Original Price: $20
Value by Year Mark: I–$20 II–$20

Count On Me

	Price Paid	Value
1.		
2.		
3.		

Days Of The Week

4.		
5.		
6.		
7.		
8.		
9.		
Totals		

1 #789704

New

Wendy
*"Wednesday's Child Is
Full Of Woe"*
Issued: 2001• Current
Original Price: $20
Value by Year Mark: I–$20   II–$20

**DICKENS
VILLAGE**

2 #617326

Bear Cratchit
*"And A Very Merry Christmas
To You Mr. Scrooge"*
Issued: 1994 • Suspended: 1996
Original Price: $17.50
Value by Year Mark:
4–$44 5–$39 6–$24

3 #614807

Gabriel

Garland

Gloria

Christmas Ghosts (set/3)
Issued: 1994 • Suspended: 1996
Original Price: $55
Value by Year Mark: 4–$100 5–$85 6–$58

4 #651362

**The Cratchit's House
(night light)**
Issued: 1994 • Suspended: 1996
Original Price: $75
Value: $95

Days Of The Week

	Price Paid	Value
1.		
Dickens Village		
2.		
3.		
4.		
5.	17⁵⁰	50⁰⁰
6.		
7.		
8.		
Totals		

5 #617296

Ebearnezer Scrooge
"Bah Humbug!'
Issued: 1994 • Suspended: 1996
Original Price: $17.50
Value by Year Mark:
4–$50 5–$36 6–$27

6 #614785

Jacob Bearly
*"You Will Be Haunted
By Three Spirits"*
Issued: 1994 • Suspended: 1996
Original Price: $17.50
Value by Year Mark:
4–$46 5–$38 6–$31

7 #617318

Mrs. Cratchit
*"A Beary Christmas And A
Happy New Year!"*
Issued: 1994 • Suspended: 1996
Original Price: $18.50
Value by Year Mark:
4–$47 5–$40 6–$30

8 #622788

**Scrooge And Marley
Counting House
(night light)**
Issued: 1994 • Suspended: 1996
Original Price: $75
Value: $120

1 #614777

Tiny Ted-Bear
"God Bless Us Everyone"
Issued: 1994 • Suspended: 1996
Original Price: $10
Value by Year Mark:
4–$38 5–$31 6–$24

DOWN STRAWBERRY LANE

2 #202991

Diane (LE-1997)
"I Picked The Beary Best For You"
Issued: 1997 • Closed: 1997
Original Price: $25
Value by Year Mark: 7–$45

3 #156329

Ella
"Love Grows In My Heart"
Issued: 1996 • Retired: 2000
Original Price: $15
Value by Year Mark: 5–$33 6–$25
7–$20 8–$17 9–$17 I–$17

4 #156337 (5) #156299

Jenna
"You're Berry Special To Me"
Issued: 1996 • Retired: 2000
Original Price: $15
Value by Year Mark: 5–$33 6–$24
7–$19 8–$17 9–$17 I–$17

Matthew
*"A Dash Of Love Sweetens
Any Day!"*
Issued: 1996 • Retired: 2000
Original Price: $15
Value by Year Mark: 5–$34 6–$25
7–$20 8–$18 9–$16 I–$16

6 #900931

**Strawberry Mini
Figurines (set/3)**
Issued: 1996 • Current
Original Price: $3.50
Value: $3.50

7 #156310

Tara
"You're My Berry Best Friend!"
Issued: 1996 • Retired: 2000
Original Price: $15
Value by Year Mark: 5–$33 6–$27
7–$20 8–$17 9–$17 I–$17

8 #156302

Thelma
"Cozy Tea For Two"
Issued: 1996 • Retired: 2000
Original Price: $22.50
Value by Year Mark: 5–$42 6–$32
7–$27 8–$25 9–$25 I–$25

FOLLOW THE RAINBOW

Dicken's Village

	Price Paid	Value
1.		

Down Strawberry Lane

	Price Paid	Value
2.		
3.		
4.		
5.	15⁰⁰	34⁰⁰
6.		
7.		
8.		
Totals		

1   #302791

Carter And Elsie
"We're Friends Rain Or Shine"
Issued: 1998 • Current
Original Price: $35
Value by Year Mark:
7–$47   **8**–$35   **9**–$35   **I**–$35   **II**–$35

2   #302775

Ellen
"You Color My Rainbow"
Issued: 1998 • Current
Original Price: $20
Value by Year Mark:
7–$33   **8**–$23   **9**–$20   **I**–$20   **II**–$20

3   #310409

Follow The Rainbow Mini Accessories (set/4)
Issued: 1998 • Current
Original Price: $10
Value: $10

4   #302767

Joyce
"Plant A Rainbow And Watch It Grow"
Issued: 1998 • Current
Original Price: $25
Value by Year Mark:
7–$31   **8**–$25   **9**–$25   **I**–$25   **II**–$25

THE FOUR SEASONS

5   #203351

Gretchen
"Winter Brings A Season Of Joy"
Issued: 1997 • Current
Original Price: $25
Value by Year Mark:
7–$33   **8**–$28   **9**–$25   **I**–$25   **II**–$25

Follow The Rainbow

	Price Paid	Value
1.		
2.		
3.		
4.		

The Four Seasons

5.		
6.		
7.		
8.		

Totals

6   #203343

Hannah
"Autumn Brings A Season Of Thanksgiving"
Issued: 1997 • Current
Original Price: $20
Value by Year Mark:
7–$28   **8**–$23   **9**–$20   **I**–$20   **II**–$20

7   #203335

Kimberly
"Summer Brings A Season Of Warmth"
Issued: 1997 • Current
Original Price: $22.50
Value by Year Mark: **7**–$35   **8**–$26
9–$22.50   **I**–$22.50   **II**–$22.50

8   #203300

Megan
"Spring Brings A Season Of Beauty"
Issued: 1997 • Current
Original Price: $20
Value by Year Mark:
7–$27   **8**–$22   **9**–$20   **I**–$20   **II**–$20

FRIENDS COME IN ALL SHAPES AND SIZES

1 #476714

Cole (1998 Gift Show Exclusive)
"We've Got A Lot To Be Thankful For"
Issued: 1998 • Closed: 1998
Original Price: $12.50
Value by Year Mark: 8–$50

2 #476714R

Cole (1998 Gift Show Exclusive, Rare Bear)
"We've Got A Lot To Be Thankful For"
Issued: 1998 • Closed: 1998
Original Price: $12.50
Value by Year Mark: 8–N/E

3 #476722

Marty (1998 Gift Show Exclusive)
"I'll Always Be There For You"
Issued: 1998 • Closed: 1998
Original Price: $12.50
Value by Year Mark: 8–$45

4 #476722R

Marty (1998 Gift Show Exclusive, Rare Bear)
"I'll Always Be There For You"
Issued: 1998 • Closed: 1998
Original Price: $12.50
Value by Year Mark: 8–$60

5 #476706

Miranda (1998 Gift Show Exclusive)
"No Matter How Blue You Feel, A Hug Can Heal"
Issued: 1998 • Closed: 1998
Original Price: $12.50
Value by Year Mark: 8–$42

6 #476706R

Miranda (1998 Gift Show Exclusive, Rare Bear)
"No Matter How Blue You Feel, A Hug Can Heal"
Issued: 1998 • Closed: 1998
Original Price: $12.50
Value by Year Mark: 8–$45

7 #476595

Tanna (1998 Gift Show Exclusive)
"When Your Hands Are Full, There's Still Room In Your Heart"
Issued: 1998 • Closed: 1998
Original Price: $12.50
Value by Year Mark: 8–$45

8 #476595R

Tanna (1998 Gift Show Exclusive, Rare Bear)
"When Your Hands Are Full, There's Still Room In Your Heart"
Issued: 1998 • Closed: 1998
Original Price: $12.50
Value by Year Mark: 8–$48

9 #846309

New

Girl Standing
Issued: 2001 • Current
Original Price: $10
Value by Year Mark: I–$10 II–$10

FRIENDS TO THE END

Friends Come In All Shapes And Sizes

	Price Paid	Value
1.		
2.		
3.		
4.		
5.		
6.		
7.		
8.		

Friends To The End

9.		
Totals		

Friends Come In/Friends To The End

99

Friends To The End/Happily Ever After

1 #846317

New

Two Girls Hugging
Issued: 2001 • Current
Original Price: $15
Value by Year Mark: I–$15 II–$15

2 #846325

New

Two Girls Standing
Issued: 2001 • Current
Original Price: $18.50
Value by Year Mark:
I–$18.50 II–$18.50

HAPPILY EVER AFTER

3 #302465

Alicia
"Through The Looking Glass, I See You!"
Issued: 1998 • Current
Original Price: $22.50
Value by Year Mark: 7–$28 8–$24
9–$22.50 I–$22.50 II–$22.50

4 #302457

Brett
"Come To Neverland With Me"
Issued: 1998 • Retired: 2000
Original Price: $22.50
Value by Year Mark: 7–$40 8–$33
9–$30 I–$26

5 #302473

Christina
"I Found My Prince In You"
Issued: 1998 • Current
Original Price: $22.50
Value by Year Mark: 7–$30 8–$26
9–$22.50 I–$22.50 II–$22.50

Friends To The End

	Price Paid	Value
1.		
2.		

Happily Ever After

3.		
4.		
5.		
6.		
7.		
8.		
9.		

Totals

6 #302481

Harvey And Gigi
"Finding The Path To Your Heart"
Issued: 1998 • Retired: 1999
Original Price: $30
Value by Year Mark:
7–$40 8–$36 9–$33

7 #302570

Kelsie
"Be The Apple Of My Eye"
Issued: 1998 • Retired: 1999
Original Price: $20
Value by Year Mark:
7–$30 8–$23 9–$23

8 #302511

Lois
"To Grandmother's House We Go"
Issued: 1998 • Current
Original Price: $22.50
Value by Year Mark: 7–$29 8–$27
9–$22.50 I–$22.50 II–$22.50

9 #476463

Pinocchio
"You've Got My Heart On A String"
Issued: 1999 • Current
Original Price: $30
Value by Year Mark:
8–$38 9–$32 I–$30 II–$30

1 #481696

Winnie
"You're My Perfect Prince"
Issued: 1999 • Retired: 1999
Original Price: $17.50
Value by Year Mark: 8–$20 9–$20

HEART STRINGS

2 #833290
New

"Best Friends"
Issued: 2001 • Current
Original Price: $10
Value: $10

3 #833991
New

"I Love You"
Issued: 2001 • Current
Original Price: $10
Value: $10

4 #833274
New

"A Kiss Makes Everything Better"
Issued: 2001 • Current
Original Price: $10
Value: $10

5 #833983
New

"U Make My Heart Smile"
Issued: 2001 • Current
Original Price: $10
Value: $10

6 #833282
New

"U R My Favorite Friend"
Issued: 2001 • Current
Original Price: $10
Value: $10

7 #833320
New

"Your Love Makes My Heart Smile"
Issued: 2001 • Current
Original Price: $10
Value: $10

HOLIDAY DANGLING

8 #176168

Ho Ho Blocks (ornament)
Issued: 1996
Suspended: 1997 • Retired: 1999
Original Price: $12.50
Value: $23

Happily Ever After	Price Paid	Value
1.		
Heart Strings		
2.		
3.		
4.		
5.		
6.		
7.		
Holiday Dangling		
8.		
Totals		

1   #176095

Holden
"Catchin' The Holiday Spirit!"
Issued: 1996
Suspended: 1997 • Retired: 1999
Original Price: $15
Value by Year Mark: 6–$24 7–$20

2   #176133

Jolene
"Dropping You A Holiday Greeting"
Issued: 1996
Suspended: 1997 • Retired: 1999
Original Price: $20
Value by Year Mark: 6–$27 7–$22

3   #176087

Joy
"You Always Bring Joy"
Issued: 1996
Suspended: 1997 • Retired: 1999
Original Price: $15
Value by Year Mark: 6–$23 7–$19

4   #176168

Joy Blocks (ornament)
Issued: 1996
Suspended: 1997 • Retired: 1999
Original Price: $12.50
Value: $25

5   #176109

Noel
"An Old-Fashioned Noel To You"
Issued: 1996
Suspended: 1997 • Retired: 1999
Original Price: $15
Value by Year Mark: 6–$27 7–$22

6   #176141

Nolan
"A String Of Good Tidings"
Issued: 1996
Suspended: 1997 • Retired: 1999
Original Price: $20
Value by Year Mark: 6–$29 7–$24

Holiday Dangling

	Price Paid	Value
1.		
2.		
3.		
4.		
5.		
6.		

John Deere

7.		

Just Between Friends

8.		

Totals

JOHN DEERE

7   #811734

New

Chuck
"You've Always Been A Deere Friend"
Issued: 2001 • Current
Original Price: $25
Value by Year Mark: 1–$25 11–$25

JUST BETWEEN FRIENDS

8   #303127

Bear With Banner
"I Miss You"
Issued: 1998
Out Of Production: 2000
Original Price: $7.50
Value: N/E

1   #303100

**Bear With Books
And Crayon**
"Forgive Me"
Issued: 1998
Out Of Production: 2000
Original Price: $7.50
Value: N/E

2   #303135

**Bear With Paint
And Brush**
"Please Smile"
Issued: 1998
Out Of Production: 2000
Original Price: $7.50
Value: N/E

3   #303097

Bear With Pillow
"I'm Sorry"
Issued: 1998
Out Of Production: 2000
Original Price: $7.50
Value: N/E

4   #303143

Bear With Scroll
"Good Luck"
Issued: 1998
Out Of Production: 2000
Original Price: $7.50
Value: N/E

5   #303119

Bear With Sign
"What A Day! Everything's Ok"
Issued: 1998
Out Of Production: 2000
Original Price: $7.50
Value: N/E

6   #303151

Mini Risers (set/3)
Issued: 1998
Out Of Production: 2000
Original Price: $12
Value: N/E

**LET HEAVEN
AND
NATURE SING**

7   #533904

Emma (LE-2000)
"Let Earth Proclaim Its Peace"
Issued: 2000 • Closed: 2000
Original Price: $20
Value by Year Mark: ▮–$26

8   #533890

Felicia (LE-1999)
"Joy To The World"
Issued: 1999 • Closed: 1999
Original Price: $20
Value by Year Mark: 9–$32

9   #533912

New

Rebecca (LE-2001)
"Let Heaven And Nature Sing"
Issued: 2001 • To Be Closed: 2001
Original Price: $20
Value by Year Mark: ▮▮–$20

Just Between Friends	Price Paid	Value
1.		
2.		
3.		
4.		
5.		
6.		
Let Heaven And Nature Sing		
7.		
8.		
9.		
Totals		

Lifetime Of Memories/Little Sparkles

LIFETIME OF MEMORIES

1 #790206

New

Billie
"A Bundle Of Joy From Heaven Above"
Issued: 2001 • Current
Original Price: $45
Value by Year Mark: ▌–$45 ▌▌–$45

2 #864374

New

"Our Journey Has Just Begun" (LE-15,000)
Issued: 2001 • Current
Original Price: $50
Value by Year Mark: ▌–$50 ▌▌–$50

LITTLE SPARKLES

3 #239720

Bear With January Birthstone
Issued: 1997 • Current
Original Price: $7.50
Value: $7.50

4 #239747

Bear With February Birthstone
Issued: 1997 • Current
Original Price: $7.50
Value: $7.50

5 #239763

Bear With March Birthstone
Issued: 1997 • Current
Original Price: $7.50
Value: $7.50

6 #239771

Bear With April Birthstone
Issued: 1997 • Current
Original Price: $7.50
Value: $7.50

7 #239798

Bear With May Birthstone
Issued: 1997 • Current
Original Price: $7.50
Value: $7.50

8 #239801

Bear With June Birthstone
Issued: 1997 • Current
Original Price: $7.50
Value: $7.50

Lifetime Of Memories

	Price Paid	Value
1.		
2.		

Little Sparkles

	Price Paid	Value
3.		
4.		
5.		
6.		
7.		
8.		
Totals		

1 #239828

Bear With July Birthstone
Issued: 1997 • Current
Original Price: $7.50
Value: $7.50

2 #239836

Bear With August Birthstone
Issued: 1997 • Current
Original Price: $7.50
Value: $7.50

3 #239844

Bear With September Birthstone
Issued: 1997 • Current
Original Price: $7.50
Value: $7.50

4 #239852

Bear With October Birthstone
Issued: 1997 • Current
Original Price: $7.50
Value: $7.50

5 #239860

Bear With November Birthstone
Issued: 1997 • Current
Original Price: $7.50
Value: $7.50

6 #239933

Bear With December Birthstone
Issued: 1997 • Current
Original Price: $7.50
Value: $7.50

LOVE LETTERS FROM TEDDIE

7 #203084

Heart Dangling Blocks
Issued: 1997
Out Of Production: 1999
Original Price: $7.50
Value: $15

8 #902950

"I Love Bears" Letters
Issued: 1997
Out Of Production: 1999
Original Price: $7.50
Value: $15

9 #902969

"I Love Hugs" Letters
Issued: 1997
Out Of Production: 1999
Original Price: $7.50
Value: $15

Little Sparkles

	Price Paid	Value
1.		
2.		
3.		
4.		
5.		
6.		

Love Letters From Teddie

7.		
8.		
9.		

Totals

1 #156515

"I Love You" Letters
Issued: 1997
Out Of Production: 1999
Original Price: $7.50
Value: $15

2 #203076

"Love" Blocks
Issued: 1997
Out Of Production: 1999
Original Price: $13.50
Value: $17

3 #240281

Love Letters Display Blocks (set/3)
Issued: 1997
Out Of Production: 1999
Original Price: $20
Value: $25

MONTHLY FRIENDS TO CHERISH

4 #914789

Alan (April)
"Showers Of Friendship"
Issued: 1995 • Retired: 1999
Original Price: $15
Value by Year Mark: 4–$47 5–$38
6–$25 7–$21 8–$17 9–$17

5 #914827

Arthur (August)
"Smooth Sailing"
Issued: 1995 • Retired: 1999
Original Price: $15
Value by Year Mark: 4–$40 5–$32
6–$26 7–$20 8–$17 9–$17

6 #914878

Denise (December)
"Happy Holidays, Friend"
Issued: 1995 • Retired: 1999
Original Price: $15
Value by Year Mark: 4–$44 5–$35
6–$24 7–$20 8–$17 9–$17

7 #914754

Jack (January)
"A New Year With Old Friends"
Issued: 1995 • Retired: 1999
Original Price: $15
Value by Year Mark: 4–$44 5–$34
6–$24 7–$20 8–$17 9–$17

8 #914819

Julie (July)
"A Day In The Park"
Issued: 1995 • Retired: 1999
Original Price: $15
Value by Year Mark: 4–$40 5–$33
6–$24 7–$20 8–$17 9–$17

9 #914800

June (June)
"Planting The Seed Of Friendship"
Issued: 1995 • Retired: 1999
Original Price: $15
Value by Year Mark: 4–$42 5–$30
6–$22 7–$20 8–$17 9–$17

Love Letters From Teddies

	Price Paid	Value
1.		
2.		
3.		

Monthly Friends To Cherish

	Price Paid	Value
4.		
5.		
6.		
7.		
8.		
9.		
Totals		

1 #914770 ②

Mark (March)
"Friendship Is In The Air"
Issued: 1995 • Retired: 1999
Original Price: $15
Value by Year Mark: 4–$42 5–$34
6–$26 7–$22 8–$19 9–$19
Variation: tail on kite
Value by Year Mark: 5–$48

2 #914797

May (May)
"Friendship Is In Bloom"
Issued: 1995 • Retired: 1999
Original Price: $15
Value by Year Mark: 4–$42 5–$32
6–$22 7–$20 8–$17 9–$17

3 #914851

Nicole (November)
"Thanks For Friends"
Issued: 1995 • Retired: 1999
Original Price: $15
Value by Year Mark: 4–$45 5–$35
6–$24 7–$20 8–$17 9–$17

4 #914843

Oscar (October)
"Sweet Treats"
Issued: 1995 • Retired: 1999
Original Price: $15
Value by Year Mark: 4–$44 5–$35
6–$24 7–$20 8–$17 9–$17

5 #914762

Phoebe (February)
"Be Mine"
Issued: 1995 • Retired: 1999
Original Price: $15
Value by Year Mark: 4–$45 5–$36
6–$25 7–$20 8–$17 9–$17

6 #914835

Seth (September)
"School Days"
Issued: 1995 • Retired: 1999
Original Price: $15
Value by Year Mark: 4–$42 5–$32
6–$24 7–$20 8–$17 9–$17

NATIVITY

7 #912980

**Angel With Bells
(ornament)**
Issued: 1993 • Suspended: 1996
Original Price: $12.50
Value: $29

8 #912980

**Angel With Harp
(ornament)**
Issued: 1993 • Suspended: 1996
Original Price: $12.50
Value: $29

9 #912980

**Angel With Trumpet
(ornament)**
Issued: 1993 • Suspended: 1996
Original Price: $12.50
Value: $29

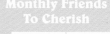

**Monthly Friends
To Cherish**

	Price Paid	Value
1.		
2.	1500	1700
3.		
4.		
5.		
6.		

Nativity

7.		
8.		
9.		

Totals

Monthly Friends To Cherish/Nativity

Value Guide — The Cherished Teddies® Collection

1 #951137

Angie
"I Brought The Star"
Issued: 1992 • Current
Original Price: $15
Value by Year Mark:
3–$64 4–$40 5–$33 6–$20 7–$17
8–$15 9–$15 I–$15 II–$15
Variation: gold metal halo
Value by Year Mark: LETTER–$90

2 #141267

Celeste
"An Angel To Watch Over You"
Issued: 1995 • Current
Original Price: $20
Value by Year Mark: 5–$36 6–$28
7–$20 8–$20 9–$20 I–$20 II–$20

3 #951218

Creche With Coverlet
(set/2)
Issued: 1992 • Current
Original Price: $50
Value: $50

4 #950688

Maria With Baby/Josh
(set/2)
Issued: 1992 • Current
Original Price: $35
Value by Year Mark:
LETTER–$95 3–$72 4–$48
5–$44 6–$40 7–$37
8–$35 9–$35 I–$35 II–$35

5 #914746

Mini Nativity With
Creche
"Cherish The King"
Issued: 1993
Out Of Production: 1995
Original Price: $32.50
Value: $95

6 #903485

Nativity
(revolving musical)
♪ *"Silent Night"*
Issued: 1993
Out Of Production: 1994
Original Price: $85
Value: $170

	Price Paid	Value
1.		
2.		
3.		
4.		
5.		
6.		
7.		
8.		
9.		

Totals

---

7 #916684

Angie   Creche With Coverlet   Maria With Baby/Josh

Nativity Collector Set (set/5)
Issued: 1993 • Current
Original Price: $100
Value by Year Mark: LETTER–$242 3–$187 4–$140 5–$128 6–$110
7–$103 8–$100 9–$100 I–$100 II–$100

8 #176362

Nativity Prayer (plaque)
Issued: 1996
Out Of Production: 2000
Original Price: $13.50
Value: N/E

9 #904309

Nativity Pull Toy, Camel
"Friends Like You Are
Precious And True"
Issued: 1993 • Retired: 1997
Original Price: $30
Value: $70

1 #651095

Nativity Pull Toy, Cow
"That's What Friends Are For"
Issued: 1994 • Retired: 1997
Original Price: $22.50
Value by Year Mark:
4–$65 5–$52 6–$47

2 #912867

Nativity Pull Toys (set/2)
Issued: 1993 • Current
Original Price: $13.50
Value: $13.50

3 #912905

Ronnie
"I'll Play My Drum For You"
Issued: 1994 • Current
Original Price: $13.50
Value by Year Mark: 4–$35 5–$27
6–$19 7–$13.50 8–$13.50
9–$13.50 I–$13.50 II–$13.50

4 #950726

Sammy
"Little Lambs Are In My Care"
Issued: 1992 • Current
Original Price: $17.50
Value by Year Mark:
LETTER–$58 3–$48 4–$40 5–$34
6–$32 7–$20 8–$17.50
9–$17.50 I–$17.50 II–$17.50

5 #950718

Edward With Donkey
Wilber With Teddy
Richard With Camel

Three Kings (set/3)
Issued: 1992 • Current
Original Price: $55
Value by Year Mark:
LETTER–$152 3–$92 4–$80 5–$63 6–$60 7–$55 8–$55 9–$55 I–$55 II–$55

6 #624772

NURSERY RHYME SERIES

Jack & Jill
"Our Friendship Will Never Tumble"
Issued: 1994 • Retired: 1998
Original Price: $30
Value by Year Mark: 3–$64 4–$50
5–$43 6–$35 7–$33 8–$32

7 #624802

Little Bo Peep
"Looking For A Friend Like You"
Issued: 1994 • Retired: 1998
Original Price: $22.50
Value by Year Mark: 3–$54 4–$46
5–$37 6–$30 7–$24 8–$24

Nativity

	Price Paid	Value
1.		
2.		
3.		
4.		
5.		

Nursery Rhyme Series

6.		
7.		

Totals

Nursery Rhyme Series/Nutcracker Suite

1 #624780

Little Jack Horner
"I'm Plum Happy You're My Friend"
Issued: 1994 • Retired: 1998
Original Price: $20
Value by Year Mark: **3**–$52 **4**–$45
5–$38 **6**–$30 **7**–$25 **8**–$24

2 #624799

Little Miss Muffet
"I'm Never Afraid With You At My Side"
Issued: 1994 • Retired: 1998
Original Price: $20
Value by Year Mark: **3**–$52 **4**–$44
5–$36 **6**–$24 **7**–$22 **8**–$22

3 #626074

Mary, Mary, Quite Contrary
"Friendship Blooms With Loving Care"
Issued: 1994 • Retired: 1998
Original Price: $22.50
Value by Year Mark: **3**–$50 **4**–$48
5–$40 **6**–$28 **7**–$24 **8**–$24

4 #624810

Tom, Tom The Piper's Son
"Wherever You Go, I'll Follow"
Issued: 1994 • Retired: 1998
Original Price: $20
Value by Year Mark: **3**–$50 **4**–$44
5–$35 **6**–$24 **7**–$22 **8**–$22

NUTCRACKER SUITE

5 #272132

Functional Nutcracker
Issued: 1997
Out Of Production: 1999
Original Price: $90
Value: N/E

Nursery Rhyme Series

	Price Paid	Value
1.		
2.		
3.		
4.		

Nutcracker Suite

5.		
6.		
7.		
8.		

Totals

6 #272388

Boy Prince   *Clara*   *Herr Drosselmeyer*   *Mouse King*

Nutcracker Suite Collector Set (set/4, LE-1997)
Issued: 1997 • Closed: 1997
Original Price: $70
Value by Year Mark: **7**–$92

7 #279641

Nutcracker Suite Furniture Figurines (set/2)
Issued: 1997
Out Of Production: 1999
Original Price: $40
Value: N/E

8 #292494

Nutcracker Suite Tree Musical
♪*"Dance Of The Sugar Plum Fairy"*
Issued: 1997 • Current
Original Price: $45
Value: $45

OLD FASHIONED COUNTRY CHRISTMAS

1   #533769

Annette
"Tender Care Given Here"
Issued: 1999 • Retired: 1999
Original Price: $20
Value by Year Mark: 8–$22 9–$22

2   #533807

Brian
"Look Out Snow! Here We Go!"
Issued: 1999 • Retired: 1999
Original Price: $22.50
Value by Year Mark: 8–$25 9–$25

3   #533823

Country Christmas Accessories (set/3)
Issued: 1999 • Retired: 1999
Original Price: $30
Value: N/E

4   #533793

Justin
"We Share Forever, Whatever The Weather"
Issued: 1999 • Retired: 1999
Original Price: $20
Value by Year Mark: 8–$23 9–$23

5   #533777

Shirley
"These Are The Best Kind Of Days"
Issued: 1999 • Retired: 1999
Original Price: $20
Value by Year Mark: 8–$23 9–$23

6   #533785

Suzanne
"Home Sweet Country Home"
Issued: 1999 • Retired: 1999
Original Price: $20
Value by Year Mark: 8–$23 9–$23

OUR CHERISHED FAMILY

7   #127922

Baby Boy
"A Gift To Behold"
Issued: 1998 • Current
Original Price: $7.50
Value by Year Mark: 7–$12 8–$9
9–$7.50 I–$7.50 II–$7.50

8   #599352

Baby Girl
"A Gift To Behold"
Issued: 1998 • Current
Original Price: $7.50
Value by Year Mark: 7–$12 8–$9
9–$7.50 I–$7.50 II–$7.50

Old Fashioned Country Christmas

	Price Paid	Value
1.		
2.		
3.		
4.		
5.		
6.		

Our Cherished Family

7.		
8.		
Totals		

Our Cherished Family

1 #624888

Father
"A Father Is The Bearer Of Strength"
Issued: 1994 • Current
Original Price: $13.50
Value by Year Mark: 3–$30 4–$26
5–$23 6–$19 7–$15 8–$13.50
9–$13.50 I–$13.50 II–$13.50

2 #127914

Grandma
"Grandma Is God's Special Gift"
Issued: 1998 • Current
Original Price: $17.50
Value by Year Mark: 7–$26 8–$22
9–$17.50 I–$17.50 II–$17.50

3 #127906

Grandpa
"Grandpa Is God's Special Gift"
Issued: 1998 • Current
Original Price: $17.50
Value by Year Mark: 7–$26 8–$22
9–$17.50 I–$17.50 II–$17.50

4 #624861

Mother
"A Mother's Love Bears All Things"
Issued: 1994 • Current
Original Price: $20
Value by Year Mark:
3–$37 4–$32 5–$28 6–$25 7–$22
8–$20 9–$20 I–$20 II–$20
Variation: "Mum" on bottom
Value by Year Mark: 4–$49

5 #624845

Older Daughter
"Child Of Love"
Issued: 1994 • Current
Original Price: $10
Value by Year Mark:
3–$28 4–$24 5–$20 6–$15 7–$12
8–$10 9–$10 I–$10 II–$10

6 #624829

Older Son
"Child Of Pride"
Issued: 1994 • Current
Original Price: $10
Value by Year Mark:
3–$26 4–$22 5–$17 6–$14 7–$12
8–$10 9–$10 I–$10 II–$10

Our Cherished Family

	Price Paid	Value
1.		
2.		
3.		
4.		
5.		
6.		
7.		
8.		
9.		
Totals		

7 #651125

Older Daughter *Older Son* *Young Son*
Father
Mother *Young Daughter*

Our Cherished Family Collector Set (set/7)
Issued: 1994 • Retired: 2000
Original Price: $85
Value by Year Mark: 3–$194 4–$155 5–$130
6–$108 7–$95 8–$90 9–$90 I–$90

8 #624853

Young Daughter
"Child Of Kindness"
Issued: 1994 • Current
Original Price: $9
Value by Year Mark:
3–$28 4–$20 5–$17 6–$13 7–$10
8–$9 9–$9 I–$9 II–$9

9 #624837

Young Son
"Child Of Hope"
Issued: 1994 • Current
Original Price: $9
Value by Year Mark:
3–$28 4–$20 5–$17 6–$13 7–$10
8–$9 9–$9 I–$9 II–$9

OUR CHERISHED NEIGHBEARHOOD

1 #352667

Christmas Decorated House
Issued: 1998
Out Of Production: 1999
Original Price: $20
Value by Year Mark: 8–$25 9–$22

2 #352691

Neighbearhood Accessories (set/3)
Issued: 1998
Out Of Production: 1999
Original Price: $15
Value: N/E

3 #352659

Winter Church Building
Issued: 1998
Out Of Production: 1999
Original Price: $20
Value by Year Mark: 8–$22 9–$22

4 #352675

Winter Post Office Building
Issued: 1998
Out Of Production: 1999
Original Price: $20
Value by Year Mark: 8–$22 9–$22

5 #352683

Winter Train Depot Building
Issued: 1998
Out Of Production: 1999
Original Price: $20
Value by Year Mark: 8–$22 9–$22

OUR CHERISHED WEDDING

6 #476315

"A Beary Special Groom-To-Be"
Issued: 1999 • Current
Original Price: $15
Value by Year Mark:
8–$17 9–$15 I–$15 II–$15

7 #476285

"Beautiful And Bearly Blushing"
Issued: 1999 • Current
Original Price: $15
Value by Year Mark:
8–$17 9–$15 I–$15 II–$15

8 #476382

"I've Got The Most Important Job!"
Issued: 1999 • Current
Original Price: $9
Value by Year Mark:
8–$9 9–$9 I–$9 II–$9

Our Cherished Neighbearhood

	Price Paid	Value
1.		
2.		
3.		
4.		
5.		

Our Cherished Wedding

6.		
7.		
8.		

Totals

Our Cherished Wedding/Paint Your Own/Radio Flyer®

1 #510254

A Beary Special Groom-To-Be

Beautiful And Bearly Blushing

Our Cherished Wedding Collectors Set (set/3)
Issued: 1999 • Current
Original Price: $50
Value by Year Mark: 8–$50 9–$50 I–$50 II–$50

2 #476323

"So Glad To Be Part Of Your Special Day"
Issued: 1999 • Current
Original Price: $10
Value by Year Mark:
8–$10 9–$10 I–$10 II–$10

3 #476374

"Sweet Flowers For The Bride"
Issued: 1999 • Current
Original Price: $9
Value by Year Mark:
8–$9 9–$9 I–$9 II–$9

4 #476366

"The Time Has Come For Wedding Bliss"
Issued: 1999 • Current
Original Price: $10
Value by Year Mark:
8–$10 9–$10 I–$10 II–$10

PAINT YOUR OWN

Our Cherished Wedding

	Price Paid	Value
1.		
2.		
3.		
4.		

Paint Your Own

5.		
6.		

Radio Flyer®

7.		

Totals

5 #662453A

**Lacey
(sold as set w/painting kit)**
"Cherish The Little Things In Life"
Issued: 1999 • Retired: 2000
Original Price: $25
Value: $27

6 #676985A

New

Trina
"My Memories Of You Are Kept In My Heart"
Issued: 2001 • Current
Original Price: $30
Value by Year Mark: I–$30 II–$30

RADIO FLYER

7 #786861

New

Booker And Fletcher
"Together, Wherever We Go"
Issued: 2001 • Current
Original Price: $28.50
Value by Year Mark:
I–$28.50 II–$28.50

1   #644382

Spanky
"Friendship Can Sometimes Be Bumpy, But It's Worth It"
Issued: 2000 • Current
Original Price: $27.50
Value by Year Mark:
9–$30   I–$27.50   II–$27.50

2   #706973

New

Vernon And Eva
"Wherever Life Takes You, I Won't Be Far Behind"
Issued: 2001 • Current
Original Price: $30
Value by Year Mark: I–$30   II–$30

SANTA EXPRESS

3   #219525

Casey
"Friendship Is The Perfect End To The Holidays"
Issued: 1996
Out Of Production: 1999
Original Price: $22.50
Value by Year Mark:
6–$39   7–$30   8–$27

4   #219177

Cindy
"This Train Is Bound For Holiday Surprises!"
Issued: 1997 • Retired: 1998
Original Price: $17.50
Value by Year Mark: 7–$36   8–$22

5   #219088

Colin
"He Knows If You've Been Bad Or Good"
Issued: 1996 • Retired: 1998
Original Price: $17.50
Value by Year Mark:
6–$33   7–$24   8–$22

6   #219118

Kirby
"Heading Into The Holidays With Deer Friends"
Issued: 1997 • Retired: 1998
Original Price: $17.50
Value by Year Mark: 7–$30   8–$21

7   #269891

Lamppost Lights (accessory)
Issued: 1997
Out Of Production: 1998
Original Price: $10
Value: $15

8   #219061

Lionel
"All Aboard The Santa Express"
Issued: 1996 • Retired: 1998
Original Price: $22.50
Value by Year Mark:
6–$36   7–$29   8–$25

9   #219312

Nick
"Ho, Ho, Ho – To The Holidays We Go!"
Issued: 1997 • Retired: 1998
Original Price: $17.50
Value by Year Mark: 7–$30   8–$22

	Price Paid	Value
Radio Flyer®		
1.		
2.		
Santa Express		
3.		
4.		
5.		
6.		
7.		
8.		
9.		
Totals		

1 #935557

Santa Express Accessory Set (set/11)
Issued: 1996
Out Of Production: 1998
Original Price: $30
Value: $40

2 #269905

Snow Bear
Issued: 1997
Out Of Production: 1998
Original Price: $12.50
Value by Year Mark: **7**–$20 **8**–$16

3 #269913

Street Lamp And Bear
Issued: 1997
Out Of Production: 1998
Original Price: $15
Value by Year Mark: **7**–$24 **8**–$20

4 #219487

Tony
"A First Class Delivery For You"
Issued: 1996 • Retired: 1998
Original Price: $17.50
Value by Year Mark:
6–$36 **7**–$29 **8**–$22

5 #219096

Toy Car
"Rolling Along With Friends And Smiles"
Issued: 1996 • Retired: 1998
Original Price: $17.50
Value by Year Mark:
6–$34 **7**–$27 **8**–$23

SANTA SERIES

Santa Express

	Price Paid	Value
1.		
2.		
3.		
4.		
5.		

Santa Series

6.		
7.		
8.		
9.		

Totals

6 #176036

Klaus (LE-1996)
"Bearer Of Good Tidings"
Issued: 1996 • Closed: 1996
Original Price: $20
Value by Year Mark: **6**–$42

7 #272140

Kris (LE-1997)
"Up On The Rooftop"
Issued: 1997 • Closed: 1997
Original Price: $22.50
Value by Year Mark: **7**–$42

8 #141100

Nickolas (LE-1995)
"You're At The Top Of My List"
Issued: 1995 • Closed: 1995
Original Price: $20
Value by Year Mark: **5**–$55

9 #534242

Sanford (LE-1999)
"Celebrate Family, Friends And Tradition"
Issued: 1999 • Closed: 1999
Original Price: $25
Value by Year Mark: **9**–$36

1 #352713

2 #706701

SANTA'S WORKSHOP

Santa (LE-1998)
"A Little Holiday R & R"
Issued: 1998 • Closed: 1998
Original Price: $22.50
Value by Year Mark: 8–$40

Wolfgang (LE-2000)
"The Spirit Of Christmas Is In Us All"
Issued: 2000 • Closed: 2000
Original Price: $25
Value by Year Mark: I–$48

3 #176079

4 #651389

5 #625434

Christmas Mini Figurines (set/3)
Issued: 1996
Out Of Production: 1999
Original Price: $15
Value: $15

Elf Riding Candy Cane (ornament)
Issued: 1995 • Suspended: 1996
Original Price: $12.50
Value: $27

Elf With Doll (ornament)
Issued: 1995 • Suspended: 1996
Original Price: $12.50
Value: $27

6 #625442

7 #141127

Elf With Stuffed Reindeer (ornament)
Issued: 1995 • Suspended: 1996
Original Price: $12.50
Value: $27

Ginger
"Painting Your Holidays With Love"
Issued: 1995 • Retired: 1998
Original Price: $22.50
Value by Year Mark:
5–$45 6–$30 7–$25 8–$25

8 #141119 (9)

Holly
"A Cup Of Homemade Love"
Issued: 1995 • Retired: 1998
Original Price: $18.50
Value by Year Mark:
5–$38 6–$26 7–$22 8–$20

#141135

Meri
"Handsewn Holidays"
Issued: 1995 • Retired: 1998
Original Price: $20
Value by Year Mark:
5–$52 6–$34 7–$25 8–$23

Santa Series

	Price Paid	Value
1.		
2.		

Santa's Workshop

	Price Paid	Value
3.		
4.		
5.		
6.		
7.		
8.		
9.	20.00	25.00

Totals

Santa's Workshop/School Days

1 #625426

**Mrs. Claus Bear
(ornament)**
Issued: 1995 • Suspended: 1996
Original Price: $12.50
Value: $28

2 #651370

Santa Bear (ornament)
Issued: 1995 • Current
Original Price: $12.50
Value: $12.50

3 #141925

**Santa's Workshop
(night light)**
Issued: 1995
Out Of Production: 1999
Original Price: $75
Value: $75

4 #141143

Yule
"Building A Sturdy Friendship"
Issued: 1995 • Retired: 1998
Original Price: $22.50
Value by Year Mark:
5–$48 **6**–$34 **7**–$25 **8**–$25

SCHOOL DAYS

5 #477036

**School Days Mini
Figurine (4 asst.)**
Boy In Baseball Hat
Issued: 1999
Out Of Production: 2000
Original Price: $7.50
Value: N/E

Santa's Workshop

	Price Paid	Value
1.		
2.		
3.		
4.		

School Days

5.		
6.		
7.		
8.		
9.		

Totals

6 #477036

**School Days Mini
Figurine (4 asst.)**
Boy With Book And Apple
Issued: 1999
Out Of Production: 2000
Original Price: $7.50
Value: N/E

7 #477036

**School Days Mini
Figurine (4 asst.)**
Girl With Apple And Flag
Issued: 1999
Out Of Production: 2000
Original Price: $7.50
Value: N/E

8 #477036

**School Days Mini
Figurines (4 asst.)**
Girl With Pom Poms
Issued: 1999
Out Of Production: 2000
Original Price: $7.50
Value: N/E

9 #477044

School Days Plaque
Issued: 1999
Out Of Production: 1999
Original Price: $8
Value: N/E

SPECIAL OCCASIONS

1 #663891

Communion
Issued: 1999 • Current
Original Price: $10
Value: $10

2 #663883

Congratulations
Issued: 1999 • Current
Original Price: $10
Value: $10

3 #663808

Graduation
Issued: 1999 • Current
Original Price: $10
Value: $10

4 #663840

Happy Anniversary
Issued: 1999 • Current
Original Price: $12.50
Value: $12.50

5 #663786

Happy Birthday
Issued: 1999 • Current
Original Price: $10
Value: $10

6 #663794

Love
Issued: 1999 • Current
Original Price: $10
Value: $10

7 #663824

Miss You
Issued: 1999 • Current
Original Price: $10
Value: $10

8 #663867

New Arrival
Issued: 1999 • Current
Original Price: $10
Value: $10

9 #663875

New Baby
Issued: 1999 • Current
Original Price: $10
Value: $10

Special Occasions

	Price Paid	Value
1.		
2.		
3.		
4.		
5.		
6.		
7.		
8.		
9.		
Totals		

Springtime Angels/Sugar & Spice

SPRINGTIME ANGELS

1 #661740

Chantel And Fawn
(set/2, LE-2000)
"We're Kindred Spirits"
Issued: 2000 • Closed: 2000
Original Price: $45
Value by Year Mark: 9–$50 I–$50

2 #661767

Daphne (set/2)
"Let Your Spirit Soar"
To Be Issued: 2002
Original Price: $35
Value by Year Mark: N/E

3 #661759
New

Willow (set/2, LE-2001)
"Cherished Your Spirit"
Issued: 2001 • To Be Closed: 2001
Original Price: $35
Value by Year Mark: I–$35 II–$35

SUGAR & SPICE

4 #352586

Missy, Cookie & Riley
"A Special Recipe For
Our Friendship"
Issued: 1998 • Retired: 2000
Original Price: $35
Value by Year Mark:
8–$37 9–$37 I–$37

5 #352616

Pamela And Grayson
"A Dash Of Love To
Warm Your Heart"
Issued: 1998 • Retired: 2000
Original Price: $22.50
Value by Year Mark:
8–$24 9–$24 I–$24

6 #352594

Sharon
"Sweetness Pours From
My Heart"
Issued: 1998 • Retired: 2000
Original Price: $20
Value by Year Mark:
8–$25 9–$22 I–$22

7 #362417

Sugar & Spice Mini
Accessories (set/6)
Issued: 1998 • Current
Original Price: $15
Value: $15

Springtime Angels

	Price Paid	Value
1.		
2.		
3.		

Sugar & Spice

4.		
5.		
6.		
7.		
Totals		

1 #352608

Wayne
"Spoonfuls Of Sweetness"
Issued: 1998 • Retired: 2000
Original Price: $20
Value by Year Mark:
8–$28 9–$23 1–$23

SWEETHEART BALL

2 #156485

Craig And Cheri
"Sweethearts Forever"
Issued: 1996 • Retired: 1999
Original Price: $25
Value by Year Mark: 5–$52 6–$37
7–$30 8–$27 9–$27

3 #156469 **4**

Darla
"My Heart Wishes For You"
Issued: 1996 • Retired: 1999
Original Price: $20
Value by Year Mark: 5–$47 6–$32
7–$27 8–$22 9–$22

#156450 **5** #156477

Darrel
"Love Unveils A Happy Heart"
Issued: 1996 • Retired: 1999
Original Price: $17.50
Value by Year Mark: 5–$44 6–$30
7–$24 8–$19 9–$19

Jilly
"Won't You Be My Sweetheart?"
Issued: 1996 • Retired: 1999
Original Price: $17.50
Value by Year Mark: 5–$47 6–$28
7–$24 8–$19 9–$19

6 #302732

Trellis Display

Katherine

Harry

King And Queen Of Hearts Collector Set
(set/3, LE-9/97-8/98)
Issued: 1997 • Closed: 1998
Original Price: $65
Value by Year Mark: 7–$82 8–$73

7 #156442 **8** #156434

Marian
"You're The Hero Of My Heart"
Issued: 1996 • Retired: 1999
Original Price: $20
Value by Year Mark: 5–$54 6–$34
7–$29 8–$22 9–$22

Robin
"You Steal My Heart Away"
Issued: 1996 • Retired: 1999
Original Price: $17.50
Value by Year Mark: 5–$52 6–$32
7–$28 8–$19 9–$19

Sugar & Spice

	Price Paid	Value
1.		

Sweetheart Ball

	Price Paid	Value
2.		
3.		
4.	8.75	44.00
5.		
6.		
7.		
8.		

Totals

121

1 #203114

Juliet *Balcony Display* *Romeo*

T Is For Teddies

Sweetheart Collector Set (set/3, LE-1997)
Issued: 1997 • Closed: 1997
Original Price: $60
Value by Year Mark: 6–$88 7–$77

② #158488A **3** #158488B **④** #158488C

Bear With A Block
Issued: 1995 • Current
Original Price: $5
Value: $5

Bear With B Block
Issued: 1995 • Current
Original Price: $5
Value: $5

Bear With C Block
Issued: 1995 • Current
Original Price: $5
Value: $5

Sweetheart Ball

	Price Paid	Value
1.		

T Is For Teddies

	Price Paid	Value
2.	5⁰⁰	5⁰⁶
3.		
4.	5⁰⁰	5⁰⁰
5.		
6.		
7.		
8.		

Totals

5 #158488D **6** #158488E

Bear With D Block
Issued: 1995 • Current
Original Price: $5
Value: $5

Bear With E Block
Issued: 1995 • Current
Original Price: $5
Value: $5

7 #158488F **8** #158488G

Bear With F Block
Issued: 1995 • Current
Original Price: $5
Value: $5

Bear With G Block
Issued: 1995 • Current
Original Price: $5
Value: $5

1   #158488H   **2**   #158488I   **3**   #158488J

Bear With H Block
Issued: 1995 • Current
Original Price: $5
Value: $5

Bear With I Block
Issued: 1995 • Current
Original Price: $5
Value: $5

Bear With J Block
Issued: 1995 • Current
Original Price: $5
Value: $5

4   #158488K   **5**   #158488L   **6**   #158488M

Bear With K Block
Issued: 1995 • Current
Original Price: $5
Value: $5

Bear With L Block
Issued: 1995 • Current
Original Price: $5
Value: $5

Bear With M Block
Issued: 1995 • Current
Original Price: $5
Value: $5

7   #158488N   **8**   #158488O

Bear With N Block
Issued: 1995 • Current
Original Price: $5
Value: $5

Bear With O Block
Issued: 1995 • Current
Original Price: $5
Value: $5

9   #158488P   **10**   #158488Q

Bear With P Block
Issued: 1995 • Current
Original Price: $5
Value: $5

Bear With Q Block
Issued: 1995 • Current
Original Price: $5
Value: $5

T Is For Teddies

	Price Paid	Value
1.		
2.		
3.		
4.		
5.		
6.		
7.		
8.		
9.		
10.		
Totals		

T Is For Teddies

① #158488R

Bear With R Block
Issued: 1995 • Current
Original Price: $5
Value: $5

2 #158488S ③

Bear With S Block
Issued: 1995 • Current
Original Price: $5
Value: $5

③ #158488T

Bear With T Block
Issued: 1995 • Current
Original Price: $5
Value: $5

4 #158488U

Bear With U Block
Issued: 1995 • Current
Original Price: $5
Value: $5

5 #158488V

Bear With V Block
Issued: 1995 • Current
Original Price: $5
Value: $5

6 #158488W

Bear With W Block
Issued: 1995 • Current
Original Price: $5
Value: $5

7 #158488X ⑧

Bear With X Block
Issued: 1995 • Current
Original Price: $5
Value: $5

⑧ #158488Y

Bear With Y Block
Issued: 1995 • Current
Original Price: $5
Value: $5

9 #158488Z

Bear With Z Block
Issued: 1995 • Current
Original Price: $5
Value: $5

T Is For Teddies

	Price Paid	Value
1.	500	500
2.		
3.	500	500
4.		
5.		
6.		
7.		
8.	500	500
9.		
Totals		

TEDDIE TRIUMPHS

Teddie Triumphs/Teddies In Motion

1 #477427

"Awesome!"
Issued: 1999 • Current
Original Price: $7.50
Value: $7.50

2 #477451

"Congratulations"
Issued: 1999 • Current
Original Price: $7.50
Value: $7.50

3 #477443

"Good Job"
Issued: 1999 • Current
Original Price: $7.50
Value: $7.50

4 #477478

"I'm Proud Of You"
Issued: 1999 • Current
Original Price: $7.50
Value: $7.50

5 #477419

"Keep Trying"
Issued: 1999 • Current
Original Price: $7.50
Value: $7.50

6 #477400

"You Did It"
Issued: 1999 • Current
Original Price: $7.50
Value: $7.50

TEDDIES IN MOTION

7 #789836

New

Andre
*"The Finish Line Is Only
A Lap Away"*
Issued: 2001 • Current
Original Price: $20
Value by Year Mark: I–$20 II–$20

8 #790192

New

Bert
*"I'm Busy As A Bee Every
Day Of The Week"*
Issued: 2001 • Current
Original Price: $20
Value by Year Mark: I–$20 II–$20

9 #477524

Chad
"With You My Spirits Soar"
Issued: 1999 • Current
Original Price: $20
Value by Year Mark:
9–$20 I–$20 II–$20

Teddie Triumphs

	Price Paid	Value
1.		
2.		
3.		
4.		
5.		
6.		

Teddies In Motion

7.		
8.		
9.		

Totals

Teddies In Motion/Through The Years

1 #477494

Dave
"An Oldy But Goodie"
Issued: 1999 • Current
Original Price: $20
Value by Year Mark:
9–$20 I–$20 II–$20

2 #477508

**Dustin and Austin
(LE-1999)**
*"Hold On For The Ride
Of Your Life"*
Issued: 1999 • Closed: 1999
Original Price: N/A
Value by Year Mark: 9–$40

3 #789844

New

Howard
"A-Farming We Will Go"
Issued: 2001 • Current
Original Price: $22.50
Value by Year Mark:
I–$22.50 II–$22.50

4 #477559

Ken
"You Make My Heart Race"
Issued: 1999 • Current
Original Price: $20
Value by Year Mark:
9–$20 I–$20 II–$20

5 #477516

Roger
"You Set My Heart In Motion"
Issued: 1999 • Current
Original Price: $20
Value by Year Mark:
9–$20 I–$20 II–$20

6 #789828

New

Warren
*"There Is No Limit To How
Far You Can Go"*
Issued: 2001• Current
Original Price: $20
Value by Year Mark: I–$20 II–$20

Teddies In Motion

	Price Paid	Value
1.		
2.		
3.		
4.		
5.		
6.		

Through The Years

7.		
8.		
9.		

Totals

**THROUGH THE
YEARS**

7 #911348

Age 1
"Beary Special One"
Issued: 1993 • Current
Original Price: $13.50
Value by Year Mark:
LETTER–$38 3–$33 4–$30 5–$25
6–$17 7–$16 8–$13.50
9–$13.50 I–$13.50 II–$13.50

8 #911321

Age 2
"Two Sweet Two Bear"
Issued: 1993 • Current
Original Price: $13.50
Value by Year Mark:
LETTER–$38 3–$33 4–$30 5–$25
6–$17 7–$16 8–$13.50
9–$13.50 I–$13.50 II–$13.50

9 #911313

Age 3
"Three Cheers For You"
Issued: 1993 • Current
Original Price: $15
Value by Year Mark:
LETTER–$38 3–$33 4–$30 5–$25
6–$17 7–$15 8–$15
9–$15 I–$15 II–$15

126

1 #911305

Age 4
"Unfolding Happy Wishes Four You"
Issued: 1993 • Current
Original Price: $15
Value by Year Mark:
LETTER–$38 3–$33 4–$30 5–$26
6–$17 7–$15 8–$15
9–$15 I–$15 II–$15

2 #911291

Age 5
"Color Me Five"
Issued: 1993 • Current
Original Price: $15
Value by Year Mark:
LETTER–$38 3–$33 4–$30 5–$26
6–$17 7–$15 8–$15
9–$15 I–$15 II–$15

3 #911283

Age 6
"Chalking Up Six Wishes"
Issued: 1993 • Current
Original Price: $16.50
Value by Year Mark:
LETTER–$42 3–$34 4–$31 5–$29
6–$23 7–$20 8–$16.50
9–$16.50 I–$16.50 II–$16.50
Variation: white elbow patch with green dots
Value by Year Mark: 7 –$46

4 #466239

Age 7
"Seven Is As Sweet As Honey"
Issued: 1998 • Current
Original Price: $16.50
Value by Year Mark:
8–$18 9–$16.50 I–$16.50 II–$16.50

5 #466247

Age 8
"Being Eight Is Really Great!"
Issued: 1998 • Current
Original Price: $16.50
Value by Year Mark:
8–$18 9–$16.50 I–$16.50 II–$16.50

6 #466255

Age 9
"Being Nine Is Really Fine!"
Issued: 1998 • Current
Original Price: $16.50
Value by Year Mark:
8–$18 9–$16.50 I–$16.50 II–$16.50

7 #466263

Age 10
"Count To Ten ... And Celebrate!"
Issued: 1998 • Current
Original Price: $16.50
Value by Year Mark:
8–$18 9–$16.50 I–$16.50 II–$16.50

8 #911356

Baby
"Cradled With Love"
Issued: 1993 • Current
Original Price: $16.50
Value by Year Mark:
LETTER–$42 3–$36 4–$33
5–$31 6–$25 7–$23 8–$18
9–$16.50 I–$16.50 II–$16.50

TUMBLING TEDDIES

9 #662135

Happiness
Issued: 1999 • Current
Original Price: $5
Value: $5

Through The Years

	Price Paid	Value
1.		
2.		
3.		
4.		
5.		
6.		
7.		
8.		

Tumbling Teddies

9.	

Totals

Tumbling Teddies/Up In The Attic

1 #662089

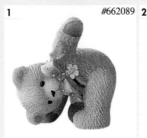

Love
Issued: 1999 • Current
Original Price: $5
Value: $5

2 #662070

Luck
Issued: 1999 • Current
Original Price: $5
Value: $5

3 #662100

Playful
Issued: 1999 • Current
Original Price: $5
Value: $5

4 #662127

Sentimental
Issued: 1999 • Current
Original Price: $5
Value: $5

5 #662119

Serenity
Issued: 1999 • Current
Original Price: $5
Value: $5

6 #662097

Wishes
Issued: 1999 • Current
Original Price: $5
Value: $5

Tumbling Teddies

	Price Paid	Value
1.		
2.		
3.		
4.		
5.		
6.		

Up In The Attic

7.		
8.		
9.		

Totals

UP IN THE ATTIC

7 #302600

Kaitlyn (LE-1998)
Old Treasures, New Memories
Issued: 1998 • Closed: 1998
Original Price: $50
Value by Year Mark: 8–$68

8 #308684

Lauren (LE-2000)
Cherished Memories Never Fade
Issued: 2000 • Closed: 2000
Original Price: $35
Value by Year Mark: 1–$55

9 #308676

Sarah (LE-1999)
Memories To Wear And Share
Issued: 1999 • Closed: 1999
Original Price: $30
Value by Year Mark: 9–$40

WE BEAR THANKS

1 #141305

Barbara
"Giving Thanks For Our Family"
Issued: 1996 • Retired: 1997
Original Price: $12.50
Value by Year Mark: 6–$35 7–$26

2 #141275

Dina
"Bear In Mind, You're Special"
Issued: 1996 • Retired: 1997
Original Price: $15
Value by Year Mark: 6–$40 7–$30

3 #141283

John
"Bear In Mind, You're Special"
Issued: 1996 • Retired: 1997
Original Price: $15
Value by Year Mark: 6–$40 7–$30

4 #141291

Rick
"Suited Up For The Holidays"
Issued: 1996 • Retired: 1997
Original Price: $12.50
Value by Year Mark: 6–$30 7–$23

5 #141542

Table With Food And Dog
Issued: 1996 • Retired: 1997
Original Price: $30
Value by Year Mark: 6–$53 7–$43

6 #175560

Displayer

Dina

Rick

Barbara   *Table With Food And Dog*   John

We Bear Thanks Collector Set (set/6)
Issued: 1996 • Retired: 1999
Original Price: $85
Value by Year Mark: 6–$185 7–$137

WINTER BEAR FESTIVAL

7 #269751

Adam
"It's A Holiday On Ice"
Issued: 1997 • Retired: 2000
Original Price: $20
Value by Year Mark:
7–$30 8–$24 9–$22 1–$22

We Bear Thanks

	Price Paid	Value
1.		
2.		
3.		
4.		
5.		
6.		

Winter Bear Festival

7.		
Totals		

1 #269778

2 #292575

3 #272884

Candace
"Skating On Holiday Joy"
Issued: 1997 • Retired: 2000
Original Price: $20
Value by Year Mark:
7–$31 8–$26 9–$22 I–$22

Festival Boy Musical Waterglobe
♪ *"White Christmas"*
Issued: 1997
Out Of Production: 1998
Original Price: $45
Value: $52

Festival Girl Musical Waterglobe
♪ *"Let It Snow"*
Issued: 1997
Out Of Production: 1998
Original Price: $45
Value: $52

4 #269786

5 #141178

6 #141178A

James
"Going My Way For The Holidays"
Issued: 1997 • Retired: 2000
Original Price: $25
Value by Year Mark:
7–$35 8–$25 9–$25 I–$25

Lindsey and Lyndon
"Walking In A Winter Wonderland"
Issued: 1997 • Retired: 2000
Original Price: $30
Value by Year Mark:
7–$42 8–$36 9–$33 I–$33

Lindsey and Lyndon
(1996 Catalog Exclusive)
"Walking In A Winter Wonderland"
Issued: 1996 • Closed: 1996
Original Price: $30
Value by Year Mark: 6–$67

7 #269735

8 #269743

Mitch
"Friendship Never Melts Away"
Issued: 1997 • Retired: 2000
Original Price: $30
Value by Year Mark:
7–$40 8–$36 9–$33 I–$33

Spencer
"I'm Head Over Skis For You"
Issued: 1997 • Retired: 2000
Original Price: $20
Value by Year Mark:
7–$30 8–$22 9–$22 I–$22

9 #269727

Ted
"Snow Fun When You're Not Around"
Issued: 1997 • Current
Original Price: $18.50
Value by Year Mark:
7–$25 8–$22 9–$22 I–$20

Other Collectibles

There's a whole other world of **Cherished Teddies** collectibles out there, just ready to be ornamental and functional at the same time. You can light your way to the Christmas tree with a **Cherished Teddies** candleholder, trim your tree with ornaments and show off your cherished family with a picture frame. And you thought they were just figurines!

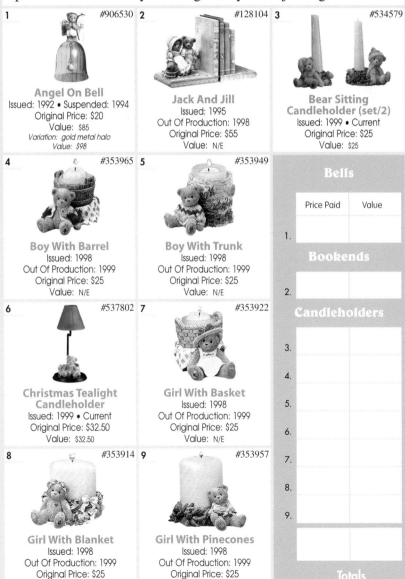

1   #906530

Angel On Bell
Issued: 1992 • Suspended: 1994
Original Price: $20
Value: $85
Variation: gold metal halo
Value: $98

2   #128104

Jack And Jill
Issued: 1995
Out Of Production: 1998
Original Price: $55
Value: N/E

3   #534579

Bear Sitting Candleholder (set/2)
Issued: 1999 • Current
Original Price: $25
Value: $25

4   #353965

Boy With Barrel
Issued: 1998
Out Of Production: 1999
Original Price: $25
Value: N/E

5   #353949

Boy With Trunk
Issued: 1998
Out Of Production: 1999
Original Price: $25
Value: N/E

6   #537802

Christmas Tealight Candleholder
Issued: 1999 • Current
Original Price: $32.50
Value: $32.50

7   #353922

Girl With Basket
Issued: 1998
Out Of Production: 1999
Original Price: $25
Value: N/E

8   #353914

Girl With Blanket
Issued: 1998
Out Of Production: 1999
Original Price: $25
Value: N/E

9   #353957

Girl With Pinecones
Issued: 1998
Out Of Production: 1999
Original Price: $25
Value: N/E

Bells

	Price Paid	Value
1.		

Bookends

2.		

Candleholders

3.		
4.		
5.		
6.		
7.		
8.		
9.		

Totals

Other Collectibles

131

Other Collectibles

1 #353973

Girl With Tree Trunk
Issued: 1998
Out Of Production: 1999
Original Price: $25
Value: N/E

2 #834179

New

Three Bears Candleholder (set/2)
Issued: 2001 • Current
Original Price: $20
Value: $20

3 #789909

New

"I'll Be Counting The Minutes 'Til We Meet Again"
Issued: 2001 • Current
Original Price: $25
Value: $25

4 #132993

Jack and Jill
Nursery Rhyme
Issued: 1995
Out Of Production: 1997
Original Price: $50
Value: N/E

5 #789887

New

"Once Upon A Time"
Issued: 2001 • Current
Original Price: $25
Value: $25

6 #156604

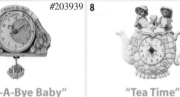

"Our Cherished Family"
Issued: 1996
Out Of Production: 1998
Original Price: $50
Value: $60

7 #203939

"Rock-A-Bye Baby"
Issued: 1997
Out Of Production: 1999
Original Price: $55
Value: N/E

8 #132977

"Tea Time"
Issued: 1995
Out Of Production: 1998
Original Price: $50
Value: N/E

9 #789895

New

"Time Flies When You're Having Fun"
Issued: 2001 • Current
Original Price: $25
Value: $25

10 #789917

New

"Too Much Work, Too Little Time"
Issued: 2001 • Current
Original Price: $25
Value: $25

11 #476951

Easter Egg (3 asst.)
Egg With Green Bow
Issued: 1999 • Current
Original Price: $10
Value: $10

12 #476951

Easter Egg (3 asst.)
Egg With Pink Bow
Issued: 1999 • Current
Original Price: $10
Value: $10

Candleholders

	Price Paid	Value
1.		
2.		

Clocks

3.		
4.		
5.		
6.		
7.		
8.		
9.		
10.		

Eggs

11.		
12.		

Totals

1 #476951

Easter Egg (3 asst.)
Egg With Yellow Bow
Issued: 1999 • Current
Original Price: $10
Value: $10

2 #156507

Easter (Dated 1996)
Issued: 1996 • Closed: 1996
Original Price: $8.50
Value: $30

3 #203017

Easter (Dated 1997)
Issued: 1997 • Closed: 1997
Original Price: $10
Value: $30

4 #203920

Baby
Issued: 1997 • Current
Original Price: $22.50
Value: $22.50

5 #203882

"Baby & Me"
Issued: 1997
Out Of Production: 1998
Original Price: $22.50
Value: $25

6 #912999

Bear With Scarf
Issued: 1993
Out Of Production: 1996
Original Price: $20
Value: $35

7 #910791

**Boy And Girl
(double heart frame)**
"Our Friendship Is Cozy"
Issued: 1993
Out Of Production: 1996
Original Price: $27.50
Value: $75

8 #911704

**Boy And Girl
(double oval frame)**
Issued: 1994
Out Of Production: 1997
Original Price: $30
Value: $52

9 #911720

Boy Praying
Issued: 1993
Out Of Production: 1999
Original Price: $20
Value: N/E

10 #902772

Boy Sailor
Issued: 1993
Out Of Production: 1997
Original Price: $20
Value: $28

11 #910783

Boy With Cat
"Friendship Shares With Their Hearts"
"You're My Forever Friend"
Issued: 1993
Out Of Production: 1993
Original Price: $19.50
Value: $50

12 #104191

Boy With Puppy
Issued: 1995 • Current
Original Price: $20
Value: $20

Eggs

	Price Paid	Value
1.		
2.		
3.		

Frames

4.		
5.		
6.		
7.		
8.		
9.		
10.		
11.		
12.		

Totals

Other Collectibles

1 #906700

Boy With Santa Cap
Issued: 1992
Out Of Production: 1995
Original Price: $20
Value: $53

2 #627364

**Bride And Groom
(invitation holder)**
Issued: 1994 • Current
Original Price: $37.50
Value: $37.50

3 #128074

"Daddy And Me"
Issued: 1996 • Current
Original Price: $25
Value: $25

4 #906700

Girl In Stocking
Issued: 1992
Out Of Production: 1995
Original Price: $20
Value: $40

5 #911712

Girl Praying
Issued: 1993
Out Of Production: 1999
Original Price: $20
Value: $35

6 #136182

Girl Reading With Doll
Issued: 1995 • Current
Original Price: $20
Value: $20

Frames

	Price Paid	Value
1.		
2.		
3.		
4.		
5.		
6.		
7.		
8.		
9.		
10.		
11.		
12.		
Totals		

7 #902772

Girl Sailor
Issued: 1993
Out Of Production: 1997
Original Price: $20
Value: $30

8 #912999

Girl With Doll
Issued: 1993
Out Of Production: 1996
Original Price: $20
Value: $39

9 #910783

Girl With Hearts
Issued: 1993
Out Of Production: 1993
Original Price: $19.50
Value: $48

10 #882208
New

**Harvest Square
Picture Frame**
At Home With Cherished Teddies
Issued: 2001 • Current
Original Price: $11
Value: $11

11 #128112

Jack And Jill
Issued: 1995
Out Of Production: 1997
Original Price: $30
Value: $40

12 #128066

"Mommy And Me"
Issued: 1996 • Current
Original Price: $25
Value: $25

Other Collectibles

1 #128082

"My Buddy And Me"
Issued: 1996
Out Of Production: 1998
Original Price: $25
Value: N/E

2 #128120

"My Cherished Family"
Issued: 1995
Out Of Production: 1999
Original Price: $25
Value: $28

3 #136174

"My Cherished Friend"
Issued: 1995
Out Of Production: 1996
Original Price: $25
Value: $35

4 #136166

"My Cherished Grandma"
Issued: 1995
Out Of Production: 1996
Original Price: $25
Value: $35

5 #135755

"My Cherished Mom"
Issued: 1995
Out Of Production: 1996
Original Price: $25
Value: $42

6 #103691

"My Cherished One"
Issued: 1995
Out Of Production: 1996
Original Price: $25
Value: $42

7 #617210

"My Visit To Santa"
Issued: 1994
Out Of Production: 1999
Original Price: $20
Value: $22

8 #624934

"Our Bundle Of Joy"
(birth record)
Issued: 1994
Out Of Production: 1999
Original Price: $20
Value: N/E

9 #476838

Wedding Photo Frame
"Our Cherished Day"
Issued: 1999 • Current
Original Price: $30
Value: $30

10 #846104

New

"Best Friends"
Issued: 2001 • Current
Original Price: $12.50
Value: $12.50

11 #846074

New

"Friends To The End"
Issued: 2001 • Current
Original Price: $15
Value: $15

12 #846112

New

"Just Us Girls"
Issued: 2001 • Current
Original Price: $12.50
Value: $12.50

Frames

	Price Paid	Value
1.		
2.		
3.		
4.		
5.		
6.		
7.		
8.		
9.		

Friends To The End Frames

10.		
11.		
12.		

Totals

135

Other Collectibles

1 #311588
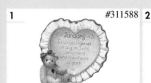

Bear With January Birthstone
Issued: 1998 • Current
Original Price: $12.50
Value: $12.50

2 #311596

Bear With February Birthstone
Issued: 1998 • Current
Original Price: $12.50
Value: $12.50

3 #311618

Bear With March Birthstone
Issued: 1998 • Current
Original Price: $12.50
Value: $12.50

4 #311626

Bear With April Birthstone
Issued: 1998 • Current
Original Price: $12.50
Value: $12.50

5 #311634

Bear With May Birthstone
Issued: 1998 • Current
Original Price: $12.50
Value: $12.50

6 #311642

Bear With June Birthstone
Issued: 1998 • Current
Original Price: $12.50
Value: $12.50

7 #311650

Bear With July Birthstone
Issued: 1998 • Current
Original Price: $12.50
Value: $12.50

8 #311669

Bear With August Birthstone
Issued: 1998 • Current
Original Price: $12.50
Value: $12.50

9 #311677

Bear With September Birthstone
Issued: 1998 • Current
Original Price: $12.50
Value: $12.50

10 #311707

Bear With October Birthstone
Issued: 1998 • Current
Original Price: $12.50
Value: $12.50

11 #311715

Bear With November Birthstone
Issued: 1998 • Current
Original Price: $12.50
Value: $12.50

12 #311723

Bear With December Birthstone
Issued: 1998 • Current
Original Price: $12.50
Value: $12.50

Little Sparkles Frames

	Price Paid	Value
1.		
2.		
3.		
4.		
5.		
6.		
7.		
8.		
9.		
10.		
11.		
12.		
Totals		

1   #675792

Baby Cradle
Issued: 2000 • Current
Original Price: $15
Value: $15

2   #675733

Ballerina
Issued: 2000 • Current
Original Price: $15
Value: $15

3   #675784

Boy Golfing
Issued: 2000 • Current
Original Price: $15
Value: $15

4   #675814

Bridesmaid
Issued: 2000 • Current
Original Price: $15
Value: $15

5   #675725

Expectant Mom
Issued: 2000 • Current
Original Price: $15
Value: $15

6   #675741

Irish Girl
Issued: 2000 • Current
Original Price: $15
Value: $15

7   #675806

**Wedding
(double heart frame)**
Issued: 2000 • Current
Original Price: $15
Value: $15

8   #675822

Wedding
Issued: 2000 • Current
Original Price: $20
Value: $20

9   #699314

Baby Boy (jointed)
♪ *"Schubert's Lullaby"*
Issued: 1994 • Suspended: 1997
Out Of Production: 1998
Original Price: $60
Value: $80

10   #699322

Baby Girl (jointed)
♪ *"Schubert's Lullaby"*
Issued: 1994 • Suspended: 1997
Out Of Production: 1998
Original Price: $60
Value: $80

11   #914320

Baby In Cradle
♪ *"Brahms' Lullaby"*
Issued: 1993 • Current
Original Price: $60
Value: $60

Special Occasions Frames

	Price Paid	Value
1.		
2.		
3.		
4.		
5.		
6.		
7.		
8.		

Musicals

9.		
10.		
11.		

Totals

137

Other Collectibles

1 #536938

Baby's 1st Christmas
♪ *"Hush Little Baby"*
Issued: 1999 • Current
Original Price: $40
Value: $40

2 #331473

Bear Ballerina
♪ *"Music Box Dancer"*
Issued: 1998 • Current
Original Price: $40
Value: $40

3 #625302

Bear In Bunny Hat (jointed)
♪ *"Here Comes Peter Cottontail"*
Issued: 1994 • Retired: 1996
Original Price: $60
Value: $92

4 #950785

Bear In Stocking Cap (waterdome)
♪ *"Have Yourself A Merry Little Christmas"*
Issued: 1992 • Suspended: 1995
Original Price: $60
Value: $120

5 #331457

Bear In Teacup
♪ *"My Favorite Things"*
Issued: 1998 • Current
Original Price: $40
Value: $40

6 #331465

Bear In Train
♪ *"Toyland"*
Issued: 1998 • Current
Original Price: $40
Value: $40

Musicals

	Price Paid	Value
1.		
2.		
3.		
4.		
5.		
6.		
7.		
8.		
9.		
10.		
11.		
12.		
Totals		

7 #900354

Bear On Rocking Reindeer (waterdome)
♪ *"Let It Snow"*
Issued: 1992 • Suspended: 1994
Original Price: $60
Value: $118

8 #912964

Bear With Toy Train
♪ *"Santa Claus Is Coming To Town"*
Issued: 1993 • Retired: 2000
Original Price: $40
Value: $42

9 #914304

Boy Praying
♪ *"Jesus Loves Me"*
Issued: 1993 • Retired: 1997
Original Price: $37.50
Value: $62

10 #699349

Bride And Groom
♪ *"Mendelssohn Wedding March"*
Issued: 1994 • Current
Original Price: $50
Value: $56

11 #912859

"Cherish The King"
♪ *"O Little Town Of Bethlehem"*
Issued: 1993 • Suspended: 1995
Original Price: $60
Value: $130

12 #903337

Christmas Bear (jointed)
♪ *"Jingle Bells"*
Issued: 1993 • Suspended: 1995
Original Price: $60
Value: $97

1 #336459

Clown On Ball
♪ *"You Are My Sunshine"*
Issued: 1998 • Current
Original Price: $40
Value: $40

2 #624926

Couple In Laundry Basket
♪ *"Love Will Keep Us Together"*
Issued: 1994 • Current
Original Price: $60
Value: $60

3 #651435

Couple In Sleigh
♪ *"Oh, What A Merry Christmas Day"*
Issued: 1994
Out Of Production: 1998
Original Price: $100
Value: $115

4 #904546

Family On Toboggan
♪ *"Jingle Bells"*
Issued: 1993 • Suspended: 1995
Original Price: $170
Value: $275

5 #707074

New

Girl On Carousel
♪ *"Minuet In G"*
Issued: 2001 • Current
Original Price: $35
Value: $35

6 #128058

Girl On Ottoman
♪ *"Au Claire De La Lune"*
Issued: 1995 • Current
Original Price: $55
Value: $55

7 #628565

Girl On Rocking Horse
♪ *"My Favorite Things"*
Issued: 1994 • Retired: 1996
Original Price: $150
Value: $195

8 #950815

Girl On Rocking Reindeer (6")
♪ *"Jingle Bells"*
Issued: 1992 • Suspended: 1994
Original Price: $60
Value: $140

9 #629618

Girl On Rocking Reindeer (12.5")
♪ *"Jingle Bells"*
Issued: 1994
Out Of Production: 1998
Original Price: $165
Value: N/E

10 #787752

New

Girl On Unicorn
♪ *"Minuet No. 3 By Bach"*
Issued: 2001 • Current
Original Price: $35
Value: $35

11 #914312

Girl Praying
♪ *"Jesus Loves Me"*
Issued: 1993 • Retired: 1997
Original Price: $37.50
Value: $60

12 #627445

Girl With Goose
♪ *"Wind Beneath My Wings"*
Issued: 1994 • Retired: 1997
Original Price: $45
Value: $83

Musicals

	Price Paid	Value
1.		
2.		
3.		
4.		
5.		
6.		
7.		
8.		
9.		
10.		
11.		
12.		
Totals		

Other Collectibles

Other Collectibles

1 #916323

Girl With Heart Harp
♪ *"Love Makes The World Go Round"*
Issued: 1994 • Retired: 1997
Original Price: $40
Value: $65

2 #903779

Girl With Muff (waterdome)
♪ *"White Christmas"*
Issued: 1993 • Suspended: 1995
Original Price: $50
Value: $110

3 #950645

Girls In Basket With Umbrella
♪ *"Let Me Be Your Teddy Bear"*
Issued: 1992 • Retired: 1997
Original Price: $60
Value: $188

4 #785326
New

Reindeer Carousel
♪ *"Jingle Bells"*
Issued: 2001 • Current
Original Price: $35
Value: $35

5 #707090

Santa With Toys
♪ *"Jolly Old St. Nicholas"*
Issued: 2000 • Current
Original Price: $35
Value: $35

6 #785334
New

Snowman With Scarf
♪ *"Deck The Halls"*
Issued: 2001 • Current
Original Price: $35
Value: $35

7 #627453

Teddie With Toy Chest
♪ *"My Favorite Things"*
Issued: 1994 • Current
Original Price: $60
Value: $60

8 #141089

Two Boys With Lantern
♪ *"The First Noel"*
Issued: 1996 • Current
Original Price: $50
Value: $50

9 #663964
Victorian Jack In The Box
♪ *"Edelweiss"*
Issued: 1999 • Current
Original Price: $40
Value: $40

10 #476900

Wedding Action Musical
♪ *"Mendelssohn Wedding March"*
Issued: 1999 • Current
Original Price: $40
Value: $40

11 #476897

Wedding (covered box)
♪ *"Mendelssohn Wedding March"*
Issued: 1999 • Current
Original Price: $30
Value: $30

12 #950777

Angel
Issued: 1992 • Suspended: 1994
Original Price: $12.50
Value: $65
Variation: gold metal halo
Value: $85

Musicals

	Price Paid	Value
1.		
2.		
3.		
4.		
5.		
6.		
7.		
8.		
9.		
10.		
11.		

Ornaments

12.		

Totals

Other Collectibles

1 #141240

Baby Angel On Cloud
Issued: 1995 • Current
Original Price: $13.50
Value: $13.50

2 #617253

**Baby In Basket
(Dated 1994)**
Issued: 1994 • Closed: 1994
Original Price: $15
Value: $38

3 #864242

New

Baby In Blanket
Issued: 2001 • Current
Original Price: $10
Value: $10

4 #913014

**Baby's First Christmas
(boy, Dated 1993)**
Issued: 1993 • Closed: 1993
Original Price: $12.50
Value: $35

5 #533300

**Baby's 1st Christmas
Photo Frame Ornament**
Issued: 1999 • Current
Original Price: $15
Value: $15

6 #913006

**Baby's First Christmas
(girl, Dated 1993)**
Issued: 1993 • Closed: 1993
Original Price: $12.50
Value: $38

7 #533343

**Baby's 1st Christmas
Rattle Ornament**
Issued: 1999 • Current
Original Price: $15
Value: $15

8 #533335

**Baby's 1st Christmas
Spoon Ornament**
Issued: 1999 • Current
Original Price: $12.50
Value: $12.50

9 #914894

**Bear In Santa Cap
(jointed)**
Issued: 1993 • Suspended: 1995
Original Price: $12.50
Value: $35

10 #950653

**Bear In Stocking
(Dated 1992)**
Issued: 1992 • Closed: 1992
Original Price: $16
Value: $58

11 #950793

**Bear On
Rocking Reindeer**
Issued: 1992 • Suspended: 1994
Original Price: $20
Value: $62

12 #706663

Bear Sitting On Moon
Issued: 2000 • Current
Original Price: $12.50
Value: $12.50

Ornaments	Price Paid	Value
1.		
2.		
3.		
4.		
5.		
6.		
7.		
8.		
9.		
10.		
11.		
12.		
Totals		

Other Collectibles

1 #537004

Bear With Blue Hat/Scarf (3 asst.)
Issued: 1999 • Current
Original Price: $7.50
Value: $7.50

2 #177768

Bear With Dangling Mittens
Issued: 1996 • Current
Original Price: $12.50
Value: $12.50

3 #537004

Bear With Green Hat/Scarf (3 asst.)
Issued: 1999 • Current
Original Price: $7.50
Value: $7.50

4 #141232

Bear With Ice Skates (Dated 1995)
Issued: 1995 • Closed: 1995
Original Price: $12.50
Value: $34

5 #537004

Bear With Red Hat/Scarf (3 asst.)
Issued: 1999 • Current
Original Price: $7.50
Value: $7.50

6 #141259

Boy And Girl With Banner
"Our First Christmas"
Issued: 1995 • Current
Original Price: $13.50
Value: $13.50

Ornaments

	Price Paid	Value
1.		
2.		
3.		
4.		
5.		
6.		
7.		
8.		
9.		
10.		
11.		
12.		
Totals		

7 #617229

Cherished Teddies In Sleigh (Dated 1994)
"Our 1st Christmas"
Issued: 1994 • Closed: 1994
Original Price: $15
Value: $36

8 #354090

Christmas Advent Calendar
Issued: 1998
Out Of Production: 1999
Original Price: $50
Value: $52

9 #272175

Dangling Snow Flake (Dated 1997)
Issued: 1997 • Closed: 1997
Original Price: $12.50
Value: $27

10 #912891

Drummer Boy (Dated 1994)
Issued: 1994 • Closed: 1994
Original Price: $10
Value: $34

11 #534161

Eskimo Holding Fish (set/2, Dated 1999 & 2000)
Issued: 1999 • Closed: 1999
Original Price: $25
Value: $30

12 #352748

Gingerbread Bear (Dated 1998)
Issued: 1998 • Closed: 1998
Original Price: $12.50
Value: $26

1 #912832

**Girl With Muff
(Dated 1993)**
Issued: 1993 • Closed: 1993
Original Price: $13.50
Value: $53

2 #865133

New

Joan
*"The Best Part Of Winter Is The
Time I Spend With You"*
Issued: 2001 • Current
Original Price: $17.50
Value: $17.50

3 #103608

"Sending You My Heart"
Issued: 1995 • Suspended: 1995
Original Price: $13
Value: $33

4 #103616

"Sending You My Heart"
Issued: 1995 • Suspended: 1995
Original Price: $13
Value: $33

5 #951226

Sister With Boots (mini)
Issued: 1992 • Suspended: 1995
Original Price: $12.50
Value: $34

6 #951226

Sister With Bow (mini)
Issued: 1992 • Suspended: 1995
Original Price: $12.50
Value: $34

7 #951226

Sister With Scarf (mini)
Issued: 1992 • Suspended: 1995
Original Price: $12.50
Value: $34

8 #865044

New

Snowbear (Dated 2001)
Issued: 2001 • To Be Closed: 2001
Original Price: $12
Value: $12

9 #176052

**Toy Soldier
(Dated 1996)**
Issued: 1996 • Closed: 1996
Original Price: $12.50
Value: $30

10 #865001

New

Two Bears Hugging
Issued: 2001 • Current
Original Price: $10
Value: $10

11 #451010

American Boy
Issued: 1998
Out Of Production: 1999
Original Price: $10
Value: N/E

12 #464120

Australian Boy
Issued: 1998
Out Of Production: 1999
Original Price: $10
Value: N/E

Ornaments

	Price Paid	Value
1.		
2.		
3.		
4.		
5.		
6.		
7.		
8.		
9.		
10.		

**Across The Seas
Ornaments**

11.		
12.		

Totals

Other Collectibles

1 #451053

Canadian Boy
Issued: 1998
Out Of Production: 1999
Original Price: $10
Value: N/E

2 #450960

Chinese Boy
Issued: 1998
Out Of Production: 1999
Original Price: $10
Value: N/E

3 #450995

Dutch Girl
Issued: 1998
Out Of Production: 1999
Original Price: $10
Value: N/E

4 #451045

English Boy
Issued: 1998
Out Of Production: 1999
Original Price: $10
Value: N/E

5 #450901

French Girl
Issued: 1998
Out Of Production: 1999
Original Price: $10
Value: N/E

6 #451002

German Boy
Issued: 1998
Out Of Production: 1999
Original Price: $10
Value: N/E

7 #450987

Indian Girl
Issued: 1998
Out Of Production: 1999
Original Price: $10
Value: N/E

8 #464112

Italian Girl
Issued: 1998
Out Of Production: 1999
Original Price: $10
Value: N/E

9 #450936

Japanese Girl
Issued: 1998
Out Of Production: 1999
Original Price: $10
Value: N/E

10 #450952

Mexican Boy
Issued: 1998
Out Of Production: 1999
Original Price: $10
Value: N/E

11 #450944

Russian Girl
Issued: 1998
Out Of Production: 1999
Original Price: $10
Value: N/E

12 #451029

Scottish Girl
Issued: 1998
Out Of Production: 1999
Original Price: $10
Value: N/E

Across The Seas Ornaments

	Price Paid	Value
1.		
2.		
3.		
4.		
5.		
6.		
7.		
8.		
9.		
10.		
11.		
12.		
Totals		

1 #450979

Spanish Boy
Issued: 1998
Out Of Production: 1999
Original Price: $10
Value: N/E

2 #450928

Swedish Girl
Issued: 1998
Out Of Production : 1999
Original Price: $10
Value: N/E

3 #707171

Bear In Cart
Issued: 2000 • Current
Original Price: $12.50
Value: $12.50

4 #707163

Bear In Sail Boat
Issued: 2000 • Current
Original Price: $12.50
Value: $12.50

5 #707147

Bear On Bunny
Issued: 2000 • Current
Original Price: $12.50
Value: $12.50

6 #707120

Bear On Cow
Issued: 2000 • Current
Original Price: $12.50
Value: $12.50

7 #707198

Bear On Elephant
Issued: 2000 • Current
Original Price: $12.50
Value: $12.50

8 #707139

Bear On Horse
Issued: 2000 • Current
Original Price: $12.50
Value: $12.50

9 #707201

Bear On Lamb
Issued: 2000 • Current
Original Price: $12.50
Value: $12.50

10 #707155

Bear On Teddie
Issued: 2000 • Current
Original Price: $12.50
Value: $12.50

11 #782653

Blue Mitten
Issued: 2000 • Current
Original Price: $10
Value: $10

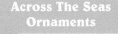

Across The Seas Ornaments

	Price Paid	Value
1.		
2.		

Antique Toys Ornaments

3.		
4.		
5.		
6.		
7.		
8.		
9.		
10.		

Wet Mitten Ornaments

11.		

Totals

Other Collectibles

Other Collectibles

1 #782718

Cream Mitten
Issued: 2000 • Current
Original Price: $10
Value: $10

2 #782645

Green Mitten
Issued: 2000 • Current
Original Price: $10
Value: $10

3 #782661

Lavender Mitten
Issued: 2000 • Current
Original Price: $10
Value: $10

4 #707406

Pink Mitten
Issued: 2000 • Current
Original Price: $10
Value: $10

5 #782688

Red Mitten
Issued: 2000 • Current
Original Price: $10
Value: $10

6 #203718

Baby
Issued: 1997
Out Of Production: 1998
Original Price: $27.50
Value: $30

7 #482064

Baby Girl With Lamb
Issued: 1999
Out Of Production: 1999
Original Price: $10
Value: $12

8 #533327

Baby's 1st Christmas
Issued: 1999 • Current
Original Price: $17.50
Value: $17.50

9 #534668

Bear In Hat And Scarf (mini)
Issued: 1999 • Current
Original Price: $12
Value: $12

10 #534668

Bear In Santa Suit (mini)
Issued: 1999 • Current
Original Price: $12
Value: $12

11 #534668

Bear With Puppy (mini)
Issued: 1999 • Current
Original Price: $12
Value: $12

Wet Mitten Ornaments		
	Price Paid	Value
1.		
2.		
3.		
4.		
5.		
Plaques		
6.		
7.		
8.		
9.		
10.		
11.		
Totals		

Other Collectibles

1 #203211

Bears With Double Hearts
Love Bears All Things
Issued: 1997 • Current
Original Price: $15
Value: $15

2 #482064

Birthday Bear
Issued: 1999
Out Of Production: 1999
Original Price: $10
Value: $12

3 #707392

Boy And Girl With Mittens
Issued: 2000 • Current
Original Price: $20
Value: $20

4 #482064

Boy Graduate
Issued: 1999
Out Of Production: 1999
Original Price: $10
Value: $12

5 #482064

Bride And Groom
Issued: 1999
Out Of Production: 1999
Original Price: $10
Value: $12

6 #104140

"Charity"
Issued: 1995 • Current
Original Price: $10
Value: $10

7 #110981

A Cherished Irish Blessing
Issued: 1995 • Suspended: 1995
Out Of Production: 1998
Original Price: $13.50
Value: $24

8 #104140

"Faith"
Issued: 1995 • Current
Original Price: $10
Value: $10

9 #627372

**"A Friend Is A Treasure
Of The Heart"**
Issued: 1994 • Current
Original Price: $10
Value: $10

10 #104116

"From My Heart"
Issued: 1995
Out Of Production: 1997
Original Price: $10
Value: $20

11 #482064

Girl And Boy With Kite
Issued: 1999
Out Of Production: 1999
Original Price: $10
Value: $12

	Price Paid	Value
Plaques		
1.		
2.		
3.		
4.		
5.		
6.		
7.		
8.		
9.		
10.		
11.		
Totals		

Other Collectibles

1 #707384

Girl With Christmas Wreath
Issued: 2000 • Current
Original Price: $17.50
Value: $17.50

2 #482064

Girls With Teddies And Cookies
Issued: 1999
Out Of Production: 1999
Original Price: $10
Value: $12

3 #882178

New

Harvest Small Plaque
Issued: 2001 • Current
Original Price: $12.50
Value: $12.50

4 #104116

"Heart To Heart"
Issued: 1995
Out Of Production: 1997
Original Price: $10
Value: $20

5 #303186

"Heaven Has Blessed This Day" (2 asst.)
Issued: 1998
Out Of Production: 1999
Original Price: $10
Value: $12

6 #303186

"Heaven Has Blessed This Day" (2 asst.)
Issued: 1998
Out Of Production: 1999
Original Price: $10
Value: $12

7 #303208

"Heaven Has Blessed This Day" (2 asst.)
Issued: 1998 • Current
Original Price: $17.50
Value: $17.50

8 #303208

"Heaven Has Blessed This Day" (2 asst.)
Issued: 1998 • Current
Original Price: $17.50
Value: $17.50

9 #627372

"Home Is Where The Heart Is"
Issued: 1994 • Current
Original Price: $10
Value: $10

10 #104140

"Hope"
Issued: 1995 • Current
Original Price: $10
Value: $10

11 #726664

"I Said An Easter Prayer" (Abbey Press Exclusive)
Issued: 2000 • Closed: 2000
Original Price: $14.95
Value: N/E

12 #627372

"Live Well, Laugh Often, Love Much"
Issued: 1994 • Current
Original Price: $10
Value: $10

Plaques

	Price Paid	Value
1.		
2.		
3.		
4.		
5.		
6.		
7.		
8.		
9.		
10.		
11.		
12.		

Totals

Other Collectibles

1 #104140

"Love"
Issued: 1995 • Current
Original Price: $10
Value: $10

2 #303054

"Mom – Maker Of Miracles"
Issued: 1998 • Current
Original Price: $15
Value: $15

3 #104116

"My Cherished One"
Issued: 1995
Out Of Production: 1997
Original Price: $10
Value: $20

4 #951005

Signage Plaque
Issued: 1992
Out Of Production: 1999
Original Price: $15
Value: $18
Variation: "Hamilton" front & understamp
Value: $79
Variation: "Enesco" on front, "Hamilton"
on understamp
Value: $88

5 #203742

"Sweet Little One Cross"
Issued: 1997 • Current
Original Price: $15
Value: $15

6 #651427

"We Bear Thanks"
Issued: 1994
Out Of Production: 1999
Original Price: $13.50
Value: $15

7 #627372

"Welcome"
Issued: 1994 • Current
Original Price: $10
Value: $10

8 #674001

Baby Angel
Issued: 2000 • Current
Original Price: $12.50
Value: $12.50

9 #673986

Boy Dressed As Clown
Issued: 2000 • Current
Original Price: $12.50
Value: $12.50

10 #674036

Boy Hugging Girl
Issued: 2000 • Current
Original Price: $12.50
Value: $12.50

11 #674087

Boy Raking Leaves
Issued: 2000 • Current
Original Price: $12.50
Value: $12.50

12 #674060

Boy With Toys
Issued: 2000 • Current
Original Price: $12.50
Value: $12.50

Plaques	Price Paid	Value
1.		
2.		
3.		
4.		
5.		
6.		
7.		

All Occasion Plaques		
8.		
9.		
10.		
11.		
12.		
Totals		

Other Collectibles

1   #674052

Girl With Roller Skate
Issued: 2000 • Current
Original Price: $12.50
Value: $12.50

2   #674028

Mom And Boy Baking Cookies
Issued: 2000 • Current
Original Price: $12.50
Value: $12.50

3   #674044

Mom With Children
Issued: 2000 • Current
Original Price: $12.50
Value: $12.50

4   #674079

Winter Boy
Issued: 2000 • Current
Original Price: $12.50
Value: $12.50

5   #176303

Angel In Red Coat
"The Season Of Peace"
Issued: 1996
Out Of Production: 1998
Original Price: $12.50
Value: N/E

6   #176346

Baby's First Christmas
Issued: 1996
Out Of Production: 1998
Original Price: $12.50
Value: N/E

7   #176117

Girl In Red Coat
"The Season Of Love"
Issued: 1996
Out Of Production: 1998
Original Price: $12.50
Value: N/E

8   #176281

Girl With Green Coat
"The Season Of Joy"
Issued: 1996
Out Of Production: 1998
Original Price: $12.50
Value: N/E

9   #176311

Our First Christmas
"Our First Christmas Together"
Issued: 1996
Out Of Production: 1998
Original Price: $12.50
Value: N/E

10   #176338

Santa With Tree And Toys
"The Season For Santa"
Issued: 1996
Out Of Production: 1998
Original Price: $12.50
Value: N/E

11   #156590

Easter (Dated 1996)
"Some Bunny Loves You"
Issued: 1996 • Closed: 1996
Original Price: $35
Value: $50

12   #203009

Easter (Dated 1997)
"Springtime Happiness"
Issued: 1997 • Closed: 1997
Original Price: $35
Value: $48

All Occasion Plaques

	Price Paid	Value
1.		
2.		
3.		
4.		

Tis The Season Plaques

5.		
6.		
7.		
8.		
9.		
10.		

Plates

11.		
12.		

Totals

1 #534196

Eskimos Holding Stars
(Dated 1999)
Issued: 1999 • Closed: 1999
Original Price: $37.50
Value: $39

2 #303046

"Mom – Maker Of Miracles"
Issued: 1998
Out Of Production: 1998
Original Price: $35
Value: $37

3 #476889

Mother's Day
Issued: 2000 • Current
Original Price: N/A
Value: N/E

4 #156493

Mother's Day
(Dated 1996)
"A Mother's Heart Is Full Of Love"
Issued: 1996 • Closed: 1996
Original Price: $35
Value: $50

5 #203025

Mother's Day
(Dated 1997)
"Our Love Is Ever-blooming"
Issued: 1997 • Closed: 1997
Original Price: $35
Value: $50

6 #141550

"The Season Of Joy"
(Dated 1995)
Issued: 1995 • Closed: 1995
Original Price: $35
Value: $50

7 #352764

"The Season Of Magic"
(Dated 1998)
Issued: 1998 • Closed: 1998
Original Price: $35
Value: $40

8 #176060

"The Season Of Peace"
(Dated 1996)
Issued: 1996 • Closed: 1996
Original Price: $35
Value: $53

9 #272183

"The Season To Believe"
(Dated 1997)
Issued: 1997 • Closed: 1997
Original Price: $35
Value: $45

10 #203726

"Sweet Little One"
Issued: 1997
Out Of Production: 1998
Original Price: $35
Value: $40

11 #272426

"We Bear Thanks"
Issued: 1997
Out Of Production: 1998
Original Price: $35
Value: $40

12 #203408

"Autumn Brings A
Season Of Thanksgiving"
Issued: 1997
Out Of Production: 1999
Original Price: $35
Value: $40

Plates

	Price Paid	Value
1.		
2.		
3.		
4.		
5.		
6.		
7.		
8.		
9.		
10.		
11.		

The Cherished Seasons Plates

	Price Paid	Value
12.		

Totals

Other Collectibles

1 #203386

"Spring Brings A Season Of Beauty"
Issued: 1997
Out Of Production: 1999
Original Price: $35
Value: $40

2 #203394

"Summer Brings A Season Of Warmth"
Issued: 1997
Out Of Production: 1999
Original Price: $35
Value: $40

3 #203416

"Winter Brings A Season Of Joy"
Issued: 1997
Out Of Production: 1999
Original Price: $35
Value: $40

4 #114901

Jack and Jill
"Our Friendship Will Never Tumble"
Issued: 1995
Out Of Production: 1998
Original Price: $35
Value: $40

5 #164658

Little Bo Peep
"Looking For A Friend Like You"
Issued: 1996
Out Of Production: 1998
Original Price: $35
Value: $40

6 #151998

Little Jack Horner
"I'm Plum Happy You're My Friend"
Issued: 1996
Out Of Production: 1998
Original Price: $35
Value: $40

7 #145033

Little Miss Muffet
"I'm Never Afraid With You At My Side"
Issued: 1996
Out Of Production: 1998
Original Price: $35
Value: $45

8 #128902

Mary Had A Little Lamb
"I'll Always Be By Your Side"
Issued: 1995
Out Of Production: 1998
Original Price: $35
Value: $40

9 #170968

Mother Goose And Friends
"Happily Ever After With Friends"
Issued: 1996
Out Of Production: 1998
Original Price: $35
Value: $45

10 #135437

Old King Cole
"You Wear Your Kindness Like A Crown"
Issued: 1995
Out Of Production: 1998
Original Price: $35
Value: $40

11 #170941

Wee Willie Winkie
"Good Night, Sleep Tight"
Issued: 1996
Out Of Production: 1998
Original Price: $35
Value: $40

12 #707260
New

Autumn
Issued: 2001 • Current
Original Price: $15
Value: $15

Cherished Seasons Plates

	Price Paid	Value
1.		
2.		
3.		

Nursery Rhyme Plates

4.		
5.		
6.		
7.		
8.		
9.		
10.		
11.		

Shadow Boxes

12.		

Totals

1 #662372

Country Charm
Issued: 2000 • Current
Original Price: $15
Value: $15

2 #662410

Happy Birthday
Issued: 2000 • Current
Original Price: $15
Value: $15

3 #662364

Oh Baby
Issued: 2000 • Current
Original Price: $15
Value: $15

4 #662399

School Days
Issued: 2000 • Current
Original Price: $15
Value: $15

5 #662402

Sports And Hobbies
Issued: 2000 • Current
Original Price: $15
Value: $15

6 #707244
New

Spring
Issued: 2001 • Current
Original Price: $15
Value: $15

7 #707252
New

Summer
Issued: 2001 • Current
Original Price: $15
Value: $15

8 #662380

Victorian Romance
Issued: 2000 • Current
Original Price: $15
Value: $15

9 #707279
New

Winter
Issued: 2001 • Current
Original Price: $15
Value: $15

10 N/A

**Easter Egg Tea Set
(Abbey Press Exclusive)**
Issued: 2000 • Closed: 2000
Original Price: $19.95
Value: $40

11 #664111

Mini Tea Set (set/6)
Issued: 2000 • Current
Original Price: $20
Value: $20

12 #534587

Boy With Holly
Issued: 1999 • Current
Original Price: $20
Value: $20

Shadow Boxes

	Price Paid	Value
1.		
2.		
3.		
4.		
5.		
6.		
7.		
8.		
9.		

Tea Sets

10.		
11.		

Stocking Holders

12.		

Totals

Other Collectibles

1 #913855

Boy With Scarf
Issued: 1993
Out Of Production: 1999
Original Price: $20
Value: $22

2 #176125

Girl With Scarf
Issued: 1996
Out Of Production: 1998
Original Price: $20
Value: $25

3 #865079

New

Photo Unavailable

Bear Mermaid (2001 Adoption Center Event Exclusive, LE-10,000)
Issued: 2001 • Current
Original Price: $30
Value: $30

Stocking Holders

	Price Paid	Value
1.		
2.		

Waterglobes

3.		

Totals

Plush

With a whopping 30+ brand-new plush critters this year, the soft and cuddly family of **Cherished Teddies** plush certainly got bigger! Sports fans everywhere will be glad to see their favorite pastimes immortalized in plush form, and no one will be able to resist the sweet-smelling *Cherished Scents* line, with their scented candles.

1   #866059
New

Autumn Outfit
Issued: 2001 • Current
Original Price: $35
Value: $35

2   N/A

Ava (1999 Avon Exclusive)
Issued: 1999
Closed: 1999
Original Price: $6.99
Value: $31

3   #644366

Baby Plush (boy)
Issued: 1999 • Current
Original Price: $15
Value: $15

4   #644366

Baby Plush (girl)
Issued: 1999 • Current
Original Price: $15
Value: $15

5   #541222

Bear w/Red Heart (1999 Gift Show Exclusive)
Issued: 1999
Closed: 1999
Original Price: $7
Value: $12

6   #888036
New

Bear With Christmas Mug (set/2)
Issued: 2001 • Current
Original Price: $15
Value: $15

7   #888044
New

Bear With Holly Mug (set/2)
Issued: 2001 • Current
Original Price: $15
Value: $15

8   #853623
New

Bear With Lunch Box (set/2)
Issued: 2001 • Current
Original Price: $25
Value: $25

9   #881775
New

Bear With Winter Mug (set/2)
Issued: 2001 • Current
Original Price: $15
Value: $15

10   #726745

"Bearing Easter Blessings" (Abbey Press Exclusive)
Issued: 2000
Closed: 2000
Original Price: $9.95
Value: $13

11   #798827
New

Beatrice
Issued: 2001 • Current
Original Price: $25
Value: $25

Plush

	Price Paid	Value
1.		
2.		
3.		
4.		
5.		
6.		
7.		
8.		
9.		
10.		
11.		
Totals		

Plush

1 #549967

Blue Bear With Ribbon (LE-48,000)
Issued: 1999
Closed: 1999
Original Price: $25
Value: $38

2 #794406

Buddy
Issued: 2000 • Current
Original Price: $25
Value: $25

3 N/A

Canadian Exclusive Bear
Issued: 2000 • Current
Original Price: N/A
Value: $14

4 #654787

Christmas Bear
♪ *"Have Yourself A Merry Little Christmas"*
Issued: 1994
Out Of Production: 1995
Original Price: $55
Value: N/E

5 #888753

New

Christmas Bear Gift Bag (set/2)
Issued: 2001 • Current
Original Price: $10
Value: $10

6 #867284

New

Christmas Tree Plush
Issued: 2001 • Current
Original Price: $15
Value: $15

7 #111414

Clown Bear
♪ *"Can't Smile Without You"*
Issued: 1995
Out Of Production: 1996
Original Price: $40
Value: N/E

8 #689599G

Diaper Bear (boy, Abbey Press Exclusive)
Issued: 2000
Closed: 2000
Original Price: $8.95
Value: $22

Plush

	Price Paid	Value
1.		
2.		
3.		
4.		
5.		
6.		
7.		
8.		
9.		
10.		
11.		
12.		
13.		
14.		
Totals		

9 #689599G

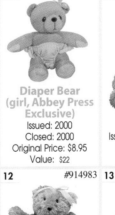

Diaper Bear (girl, Abbey Press Exclusive)
Issued: 2000
Closed: 2000
Original Price: $8.95
Value: $22

10 #790605

Doris
Issued: 2000 • Current
Original Price: $25
Value: $25

11 #914975

Elsa
"We'll Always Be Special Friends"
Issued: 1993
Out Of Production: 1996
Original Price: $50
Value: N/E

12 #914983

Elsa
"I'll Always Be Here For You"
Issued: 1993
Out Of Production: 1996
Original Price: $25
Value: N/E

13 #914991

Elsa
"I'll Always Be Here For You"
Issued: 1993
Out Of Production: 1996
Original Price: $15
Value: N/E

14 #798487

New

Frosty And Aurora
Issued: 2001 • Current
Original Price: $35
Value: $35

Plush

1 #644323

Girl With Christmas Ribbon
Issued: 1999 • Current
Original Price: $15
Value: $15

2 #644323

Girl With Christmas Ribbon
Issued: 1999 • Current
Original Price: $15
Value: $15

3 #644323

Girl With Christmas Ribbon
Issued: 1999 • Current
Original Price: $15
Value: $15

4 #790613

New

Grumps
Issued: 2001 • Current
Original Price: $25
Value: $25

5 #867292

New

Hanging Ornament Plush
Issued: 2001 • Current
Original Price: $15
Value: $15

6 #888737

New

Holly Bear Gift Bag (set/2)
Issued: 2001 • Current
Original Price: $10
Value: $10

7 #811971

New

Homecoming Collector Plush
Issued: 2001 • Current
Original Price: $25
Value: $25

8 #631736

Jackie
Issued: 1999
Out Of Production: 2000
Original Price: $25
Value: $27

9 #649155

Jennifer (LE-1999)
Issued: 1999
Closed: 1999
Original Price: $25
Value: $28

10 #867268

New

Jingle Bell Plush
Issued: 2001 • Current
Original Price: $15
Value: $15

11 #649155

John (LE-1999)
Issued: 1999
Closed: 1999
Original Price: $25
Value: $30

12 #631736

Karen
Issued: 1999
Out Of Production: 2000
Original Price: $25
Value: $27

13 #798479

New

Merry
Issued: 2001 • Current
Original Price: $25
Value: $25

14 #662321

Millennium Event Bears (set/2)
Issued: 1999
Closed: 2000
Original Price: $27.50
Value: N/E

Plush		
	Price Paid	Value
1.		
2.		
3.		
4.		
5.		
6.		
7.		
8.		
9.		
10.		
11.		
12.		
13.		
14.		
Totals		

Plush

1 #916692

Norman
*"We'll Always Be
Special Friends"*
Issued: 1993
Out Of Production: 1996
Original Price: $65
Value: N/E

2 #916706

Norman
*"We'll Always Be
Special Friends"*
Issued: 1993
Out Of Production: 1996
Original Price: $45
Value: $70

3 #916714

Norman
*"We'll Always Be
Special Friends"*
Issued: 1993
Out Of Production: 1996
Original Price: $30
Value: N/E

4 #916730

Norman
*"We'll Always Be
Special Friends"*
♪ *"Teddie Bear Picnic"*
Issued: 1993
Out Of Production: 1996
Original Price: $60
Value: N/E

5 #639206

**Rodney (Gift-To-Go
Exclusive, sold as
set, #646504,
w/figurine)**
Issued: 1999
Closed: 1999
Original Price: $25
Value: $30

6 #873446

New

Roly Poly Santa
Issued: 2001 • Current
Original Price: $35
Value: $35

7 #666696

St. Jude Plush
Issued: 2000 • Current
Original Price: $10
Value: $10

8 #610585

**Santa With Hat(Gift
Show Exclusive)**
Issued: 1999
Closed: 1999
Original Price: $7
Value: $12

9 #631736

Sara
Issued: 1999
Out Of Production: 2000
Original Price: $25
Value: $27

10 #866032

New

**Spring Sailor
Plush**
Issued: 2001 • Current
Original Price: $35
Value: $35

11 #867276

New

Star Plush
Issued: 2001 • Current
Original Price: $15
Value: $15

12 #866040

New

**Summer Sundress
Plush**
Issued: 2001 • Current
Original Price: $35
Value: $35

13 #790702

Toys For Tots' Plush
Issued: 2000 • Current
Original Price: $2
Value: $2

14 #662291

Val
Issued: 1999
Closed: 1999
Original Price: $27.50
Value: $30

Plush

	Price Paid	Value
1.		
2.		
3.		
4.		
5.		
6.		
7.		
8.		
9.		
10.		
11.		
12.		
13.		
14.		

Totals

1 #662291L

**Val
(Limited Edition)**
Issued: 1999
Closed: 1999
Original Price: $27.50
Value: $33

2 #789925

New

Wanda
Issued: 2001 • Current
Original Price: $25
Value: $25

3 #882119

New

**Winter Bear
Gift Bag (set/2)**
Issued: 2001 • Current
Original Price: $10
Value: $10

4 #866067

New

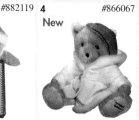

**Winter Outfit
Plush**
Issued: 2001 • Current
Original Price: $35
Value: $35

5 #726753

**XOXO (Abbey
Press Exclusive)**
Issued: 2000
Closed: 2000
Original Price: $9.95
Value: $25

6 #708569

American Boy
Issued: 2000 • Current
Original Price: $10
Value: $10

7 #708593

Dutch Girl
Issued: 2000 • Current
Original Price: $10
Value: $10

8 #708615

German Boy
Issued: 2000 • Current
Original Price: $10
Value: $10

9 #708623

Indian Girl
Issued: 2000 • Current
Original Price: $10
Value: $10

10 #708631

Irish Girl
Issued: 2000 • Current
Original Price: $10
Value: $10

11 #708658

Italian Girl
Issued: 2000 • Current
Original Price: $10
Value: $10

12 #708666

Mexican Boy
Issued: 2000 • Current
Original Price: $10
Value: $10

13 #708674

Russian Girl
Issued: 2000 • Current
Original Price: $10
Value: $10

14 #770108

New

Ivory
Issued: 2001 • Current
Original Price: $7
Value: $7

Plush		
	Price Paid	Value
1.		
2.		
3.		
4.		
5.		
Across The Seas		
6.		
7.		
8.		
9.		
10.		
11.		
12.		
13.		
Cherished Scents		
14.		
Totals		

Plush

1 #770094
New
Jasmine
Issued: 2001 • Current
Original Price: $7
Value: $7

2 #770140
New
Lavender
Issued: 2001 • Current
Original Price: $7
Value: $7

3 #770132
New
Orchid
Issued: 2001 • Current
Original Price: $7
Value: $7

4 #770116
New
Peach
Issued: 2001 • Current
Original Price: $7
Value: $7

5 #770124
New
Rose
Issued: 2001 • Current
Original Price: $7
Value: $7

6 #637998
4th Of July
Issued: 1999 • Current
Original Price: $7
Value: $7

7 #638021
Christmas
Issued: 1999 • Current
Original Price: $7
Value: $7

8 #637955
Easter
Issued: 1999 • Current
Original Price: $7
Value: $7

Cherished Scents

	Price Paid	Value
1.		
2.		
3.		
4.		
5.		

Holiday Occasions

6.		
7.		
8.		
9.		
10.		
11.		
12.		
13.		
14.		

Totals

9 #638005
Halloween
Issued: 1999 • Current
Original Price: $7
Value: $7

10 #637963
Mother's Day
Issued: 1999 • Current
Original Price: $7
Value: $7

11 #637696
New Year's
Issued: 1999 • Current
Original Price: $7
Value: $7

12 #637947
St. Patrick's Day
Issued: 1999 • Current
Original Price: $7
Value: $7

13 #637971
Teacher
Issued: 1999 • Current
Original Price: $7
Value: $7

14 #638013
Thanksgiving
Issued: 1999 • Current
Original Price: $7
Value: $7

Plush

1   #637939   **2**   #556165   **3**   #556181   **4**   #556203

Valentine	January	February	March
Issued: 1999 • Current	Issued: 1999 • Current	Issued: 1999 • Current	Issued: 1999 • Current
Original Price: $7	Original Price: $7	Original Price: $7	Original Price: $7
Value: $7	Value: $7	Value: $7	Value: $7

5   #556246   **6**   #556270   **7**   #556289   **8**   #556327

April	May	June	July
Issued: 1999 • Current	Issued: 1999 • Current	Issued: 1999 • Current	Issued: 1999 • Current
Original Price: $7	Original Price: $7	Original Price: $7	Original Price: $7
Value: $7	Value: $7	Value: $7	Value: $7

9   #556483   **10**   #556688   **11**   #556750

August	September	October
Issued: 1999 • Current	Issued: 1999 • Current	Issued: 1999 • Current
Original Price: $7	Original Price: $7	Original Price: $7
Value: $7	Value: $7	Value: $7

12   #556785   **13**   #556793   **14**   #662240

November	December	Bear On Bear
Issued: 1999 • Current	Issued: 1999 • Current	Issued: 2000 • Current
Original Price: $7	Original Price: $7	Original Price: $17.50
Value: $7	Value: $7	Value: $17.50

Holiday Occasions

	Price Paid	Value
1.		

Monthly Plush

2.		
3.		
4.		
5.		
6.		
7.		
8.		
9.		
10.		
11.		
12.		
13.		

Pull-Along Plush

14.		

Totals

Plush

1 #737399

Bear On Bunny
Issued: 2000 • Current
Original Price: $17.50
Value: $17.50

2 #662259

Bear On Cow
Issued: 2000 • Current
Original Price: $17.50
Value: $17.50

3 #662275

Bear On Elephant
Issued: 2000 • Current
Original Price: $17.50
Value: $17.50

4 #662267

Bear On Horse
Issued: 2000 • Current
Original Price: $17.50
Value: $17.50

5 #742740

Bear On Lamb
Issued: 2000 • Current
Original Price: $17.50
Value: $17.50

6 #737380

Bear In Sail Boat
Issued: 2000 • Current
Original Price: $17.50
Value: $17.50

7 #661597

Radio Flyer®/America's Promise®
Issued: 2000 • Current
Original Price: $30
Value: $30

8 #505374

"Best Friends"
Issued: 1999 • Current
Original Price: $7
Value: $7

Pull-Along Plush

	Price Paid	Value
1.		
2.		
3.		
4.		
5.		
6.		
Radio Flyer		
7.		
T-shirt Teddies		
8.		
9.		
10.		
11.		
12.		
13.		
Sports Teddies		
14.		
Totals		

9 #505358

"Hug Me"
Issued: 1999 • Current
Original Price: $7
Value: $7

10 #505390

"I Need You"
Issued: 1999 • Current
Original Price: $7
Value: $7

11 #505331

"Love Me"
Issued: 1999 • Current
Original Price: $7
Value: $7

12 #505323

"Miss You"
Issued: 1999 • Current
Original Price: $7
Value: $7

13 #505382

"Smile"
Issued: 1999 • Current
Original Price: $7
Value: $7

14 #790257

New

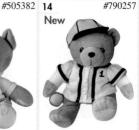

Baseball
Issued: 2001 • Current
Original Price: $8
Value: $8

1   #790723

New

Basketball
Issued: 2001 • Current
Original Price: $8
Value: $8

2   #790281

New

Cheerleader
Issued: 2001 • Current
Original Price: $8
Value: $8

3   #790311

New

Football
Issued: 2001 • Current
Original Price: $8
Value: $8

4   #790303

New

Soccer
Issued: 2001 • Current
Original Price: $8
Value: $8

Sports Teddies

	Price Paid	Value
1.		
2.		
3.		
4.		
Totals		

Cherished Teddies Club™

This year's **Cherished Teddies** *Club* drama is a mystery – a whodunnit, to be precise! A Bearywood thriller, a mysterious disappearance, a cast of glamorous characters and an exciting plot make up a whole new line of fabulous collectibles. From figurines to lapel pins to postcards, you'll be in on the mystery before anyone can solve it!

2001

1 #824313

New

2001 Membearship Lapel Pin (pink w/"Crew Member", 2001 Lapel Pin)
Issued: 2001 • To Be Closed: 2001
Membearship Gift
Value: N/E

2 #824313C

New

Photo Unavailable

2001 Membearship Lapel Pin (turquoise w/ "Charter Crew Member," 2001 Charter Lapel Pin)
Issued: 2001 • To Be Closed: 2001
Membearship Gift
Value: N/E

3 #824305

New

Angelo Bearcino (Customer Appreciation Figurine)
Issued: 2001 • To Be Closed: 2001
Membearship Gift
Value: N/E

4 #CT011

New

Deena Wilde (Membears Only Figurine)
Issued: 2001 • To Be Closed: 2001
Original Price: $25
Value: $25

5 #CT012

New

Giacomo "Jake" Bearcino (Membears Only Figurine)
Issued: 2001 • To Be Closed: 2001
Original Price: $15
Value: $15

6 #CT013

New

Maxine D'Face (Membears Only Figurine)
Issued: 2001 • To Be Closed: 2001
Original Price: $25
Value: $25

7 #824291

New

Mystery Bear (Early Renewal Figurine)
Issued: 2001 • To Be Closed: 2001
Membearship Gift
Value: N/E

8 #CT107

New

Photo Unavailable

T. James Bear (w/ blue coat and black briefcase, 2001 Charter Membearship Figurine)
Issued: 2001 • To Be Closed: 2001
Membearship Gift
Value: N/E

2001 Collector's Club

	Price Paid	Value
1.		
2.		
3.		
4.		
5.		
6.		
7.		
8.		
Totals		

Collector's Club

1 #CT007

New

T James Bear (w/ yellow coat and silver briefcase, 2001 Membearship Figurine)
Issued: 2001 • To Be Closed: 2001
Membearship Gift
Value: N/E

2

New

TravelBear Postcards
Issued: 2001 • To Be Closed: 2001
Membearship Gift
Value: N/E

2000

3 #708437

2000 Membearship Lapel Pin (w/blue bow tie, 2000 Lapel Pin)
Issued: 2000 • Closed: 2000
Membearship Gift
Value: N/E

4 #708437K

2000 Membearship Lapel Pin (w/red bow tie, 2000 Charter Lapel Pin)
Issued: 2000 • Closed: 2000
Membearship Gift
Value: N/E

5 #685968

Audrey D. Zeiner (Membears Only Figurine)
Issued: 2000 • Closed: 2000
Original Price: 22.50
Value: $42

6 #685976

Brad Wheeler as Troy "Mac" McBear (Membears Only Figurine)
Issued: 2000 • Closed: 2000
Original Price: $25
Value: $33

7 N/A

Collectible Print of Julia Bearon with Bookmark
Issued: 2000 • Closed: 2000
Membearship Gift
Value: N/E

8 N/A

Julia Bearon as Gloria Growlette (w/black dog, 2000 Membearship Figurine)
Issued: 2000 • Closed: 2000
Membearship Gift
Value: N/E

9 #685747

Julia Bearon as Gloria Growlette (w/white dog, 2000 Charter Membearship Figurine)
Issued: 2000 • Closed: 2000
Membearship Gift
Value: $30

10 #685771

Marco Pawllini, Bear-ector (Membears Only Figurine)
Issued: 2000 • Closed: 2000
Original Price: $20
Value: $33

11 N/A

Neil (Promotional piece, sold as set)
One Small Step For Love, One Giant Leap For Friendship
Issued: 2000 • Closed: 2000
Original Price: $30
Value: $37

2001 Collector's Club

	Price Paid	Value
1.		
2.		

2000 Collector's Club

3.		
4.		
5.		
6.		
7.		
8.		
9.		
10.		
11.		
Totals		

Collector's Club

1 #731765

Photo
Unavailable

**Ricky McBear
(2000 Membear Get
Membear Figurine)**
Issued: 2000 • Closed: 2000
Membearship Gift
Value: N/E

1999

2 #CT994

**1999 Membears
Only Float**
Issued: 1999 • Closed: 1999
Original Price: $60
Value: N/E

3 #556955

**Exclusive 5th
Anniversary Mini
Figurine**
Issued: 1999 • Closed: 1999
Membearship Gift
Value: N/E

4 #CT005

**Lanny (w/blue letters,
1999 Membearship
Figurine)**
Issued: 1999 • Closed: 1999
Membearship Gift
Value: $36

5 #CT105

**Lanny (w/red letters,
1999 Charter
Membearship Figurine)**
Issued: 1999 • Closed: 1999
Membearship Gift
Value: $40

2000 Collector's Club

	Price Paid	Value
1.		

1999 Collector's Club

2.		
3.		
4.		
5.		
6.		
7.		
8.		
9.		
10.		
11.		
Totals		

6 #CT993

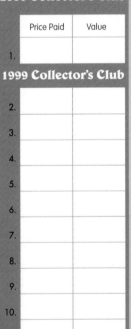

**Letty
(1999 Membearship
Figurine)**
Issued: 1999 • Closed: 1999
Original Price: $22.50
Value: $36

7 #631345

**Ray (1999 Customer
Appreciation Figurine)**
*Special Treats Make
Life Complete*
Issued: 1999 • Closed: 1999
Membearship Gift
Value: $92

8 #CT305

**Sculpted Lapel Pin
(gold tone, 1999 Charter
Lapel Pin)**
Issued: 1999 • Closed: 1999
Membearship Gift
Value: N/E

9 #CT205

**Sculpted Lapel Pin (silver
tone, 1999 Lapel Pin)**
Issued: 1999 • Closed: 1999
Membearship Gift
Value: N/E

10 #CT992

**Vivienne (1999 Membears
Only Figurine)**
Issued: 1999 • Closed: 1999
Original Price: $17.50
Value: $33

11 #CT991

**Walter (1999 Membears
Only Figurine)**
Issued: 1999 • Closed: 1999
Original Price: $17.50
Value: $33

1998

1 N/A

**Bubbie Waterton
(1998 Membear Get
Membear Figurine)**
Issued: 1998 • Closed: 1998
Original Price: N/A
Value: $38

2 #CRT442

**Cherished Teddies Club
"Bear Tag" Necklace**
Issued: 1998 • Closed: 1998
Membearship Gift
Value: N/E

3 #CT983

**Cherished Teddies Town
Accessory Set (set/3,
1998 Membears Only Set)**
Issued: 1998 • Closed: 1998
Original Price: $17.50
Value: $20

4 #CRT466

**Cherished Teddies Town
Teddie Care Center/
Ambulance Easel
Display (set/2)**
Issued: 1998 • Closed: 1998
Membership Gift
Value: N/E

5 #CT104

**Dr. Darlene Makebetter
(w/pink bag, 1998
Charter Membearship
Figurine)**
Issued: 1998 • Closed: 1998
Membearship Gift
Value: $38

6 #CT004

**Dr. Darlene Makebetter
(w/yellow bag, 1998
Membearship Figurine)**
Issued: 1998 • Closed: 1998
Membearship Gift
Value: $38

7 #CT981

**Lela Nightingale (1998
Membears Only Figurine)**
Issued: 1998 • Closed: 1998
Original Price: $15
Value: $40

8 #CT982

**Wade Weathersbee
(1998 Membears Only
Figurine)**
Issued: 1998 • Closed: 1998
Original Price: $13.50
Value: $40

1997

9 #273554

**Amelia (Cherished
Rewards, Level #2)**
Issued: 1997 • Closed: 1998
Original Price: N/A
Value: $70

10 #273198

**Benny (Cherished
Rewards, Level #1)**
Issued: 1997 • Closed: 1998
Original Price: N/A
Value: $58

1998 Collector's Club

	Price Paid	Value
1.		
2.		
3.		
4.		
5.		
6.		
7.		
8.		

1997 Collector's Club

9.		
10.		
Totals		

167

Collector's Club

1 #CT972

Bernard and Bernice Beary (1997 Membears Only Figurine)
Issued: 1997 • Closed: 1997
Original Price: $17.50
Value: $40

2 #297550

Blaire Beary (Gift Club Membearship Piece)
Issued: 1997 • Closed: 1997
Membearship Gift
Value: $45

3 #CRT279

Cherished Teddies Club Membearship Pin
Issued: 1997 • Closed: 1997
Membearship Gift
Value: $11

4 #CRT289

Cherished Teddies Town Depot Easel
Issued: 1997 • Closed: 1997
Membearship Gift
Value: $11

5 #CT971

Eleanor P. Beary (1997 Membears Only Figurine)
Issued: 1997 • Closed: 1997
Original Price: $17.50
Value: $40

6 #CT103

Lloyd (w/green suitcase, 1997 Charter Membears Only Figurine)
Issued: 1997 • Closed: 1997
Membearship Gift
Value: $48

1997 Collector's Club

	Price Paid	Value
1.		
2.		
3.		
4.		
5.		
6.		
7.		
8.		

1996 Collector's Club

9.		
10.		
11.		

| Totals | | |

7 #CT003

Lloyd (w/red suitcase, 1997 Membears Only Figurine)
Issued: 1997 • Closed: 1997
Membearship Gift
Value: $42

8 #277002

Mary Jane (Cherished Rewards, Level #3)
Issued: 1997 • Closed: 1998
Original Price: N/A
Value: $120

9 #CRT124

Cherished Teddies Club Membearship Pin
Issued: 1996 • Closed: 1996
Membearship Gift
Value: $18

1996

10 #CT962

Emily E. Claire (1996 Membears Only Figurine)
Issued: 1996 • Closed: 1996
Original Price: $17.50
Value: $46

11 #CRT122

Hartford Printing Co., Firehouse #1 And The Honey Buns Shop Backdrop
Issued: 1996 • Closed: 1996
Membearship Gift
Value: $13

1 #CT961

Kurtis D. Claw (1996 Membears Only Figurine)
Issued: 1996 • Closed: 1996
Original Price: $17.50
Value: $50

2 #CT102

R. Harrison Hartford (w/red pencil, 1996 Charter Membearship Figurine)
Issued: 1996 • Closed: 1996
Membership Gift
Value: $58

3 #CT002

R. Harrison Hartford (w/yellow pencil, 1996 Membearship Figurine)
Issued: 1996 • Closed: 1996
Membearship Gift
Value: $52

4 #CT953

Town Tattler Night Light (1996 Membears Only Figurine)
Issued: 1996 • Closed: 1996
Original Price: $50
Value: $78

1995

5 #CRT064

Cherished Teddies Town Backdrop
Issued: 1995 • Closed: 1995
Membearship Gift
Value: $18

6 #CT001

Cub E. Bear (1995 Membearship Figurine)
Issued: 1995 • Closed: 1995
Membearship Gift
Value: $55

7 #CT952

Hilary Hugabear (1995 Membears Only Figurine)
Issued: 1995 • Closed: 1995
Original Price: $17.50
Value: $77

8 #CRT065

Key To Cherished Teddies Town (pin)
Issued: 1995 • Closed: 1995
Membearship Gift
Value: $17

9 #CT951

Mayor Wilson T. Beary (1995 Membears Only Figurine)
Issued: 1995 • Closed: 1995
Original Price: $20
Value: $70

1996 Collector's Club

	Price Paid	Value
1.		
2.		
3.		
4.		

1995 Collector's Club

5.		
6.		
7.		
8.		
9.		
Totals		

Future Releases

Check our website, *CollectorsQuest.com*, for new product releases and record the information here.

Cherished Teddies®	Item #	Production Mark	Price Paid	Value

	Price Paid	Value
Page Total:		

Future Releases

Check our website, *CollectorsQuest.com*, for new product releases and record the information here.

Cherished Teddies®	Item #	Production Mark	Price Paid	Value

	Price Paid	Value
Page Total:		

Total Value Of My Collection

Record your collection here by adding the totals from
the bottom of each Value Guide page.

CHERISHED TEDDIES®

Page Number	Price Paid	Value
Page 35		
Page 36		
Page 37		
Page 38		
Page 39		
Page 40		
Page 41		
Page 42		
Page 43		
Page 44		
Page 45		
Page 46		
Page 47		
Page 48		
Page 49		
Page 50		
Page 51		
Page 52		
Page 53		
Page 54		
Page 55		
Page 56		
Subtotal:		

CHERISHED TEDDIES®

Page Number	Price Paid	Value
Page 57		
Page 58		
Page 59		
Page 60		
Page 61		
Page 62		
Page 63		
Page 64		
Page 65		
Page 66		
Page 67		
Page 68		
Page 69		
Page 70		
Page 71		
Page 72		
Page 73		
Page 74		
Page 75		
Page 76		
Page 77		
Page 78		
Subtotal:		

	Price Paid	Value
Total:		

Total Value Of My Collection

Record your collection here by adding the totals from
the bottom of each Value Guide page.

CHERISHED TEDDIES®			CHERISHED TEDDIES®		
Page Number	Price Paid	Value	Page Number	Price Paid	Value
Page 79			Page 101		
Page 80			Page 102		
Page 81			Page 103		
Page 82			Page 104		
Page 83			Page 105		
Page 84			Page 106		
Page 85			Page 107		
Page 86			Page 108		
Page 87			Page 109		
Page 88			Page 110		
Page 89			Page 111		
Page 90			Page 112		
Page 91			Page 113		
Page 92			Page 114		
Page 93			Page 115		
Page 94			Page 116		
Page 95			Page 117		
Page 96			Page 118		
Page 97			Page 119		
Page 98			Page 120		
Page 99			Page 121		
Page 100			Page 122		
Subtotal:			Subtotal:		
			Total:	Price Paid	Value

Total Value Of My Collection

Record your collection here by adding the totals from
the bottom of each Value Guide page.

CHERISHED TEDDIES®			CHERISHED TEDDIES®		
Page Number	Price Paid	Value	Page Number	PricePaid	Value
Page 123			Page 147		
Page 124			Page 148		
Page 125			Page 149		
Page 126			Page 150		
Page 127			Page 151		
Page 128			Page 152		
Page 129			Page 153		
Page 130			Page 154		
Page 131			Page 155		
Page 132			Page 156		
Page 133			Page 157		
Page 134			Page 158		
Page 135			Page 159		
Page 136			Page 160		
Page 137			Page 161		
Page 138			Page 162		
Page 139			Page 163		
Page 140			Page 164		
Page 141			Page 165		
Page 142			Page 166		
Page 143			Page 167		
Page 144			Page 168		
Page 145			Page 169		
Page 146			Subtotal:		
Subtotal:					

	Price Paid	Value
Total:		

Teddies, Teddies Everywhere: Other Products

Following is a listing of the **Cherished Teddies** accessories which have been produced to date. New products for 2001 are marked with an asterisk (*), while those which have gone out of production are marked with an "O/P."

Bear-ettes

- ❏ Bears With Bows Hair Pins (O/P) 273600
- ❏ Brown-Eyed Susan (O/P) 273570
- ❏ Girl With Bow/Heart (O/P) 273597
- ❏ Girl With Purple Ribbon (O/P) 273619
- ❏ Girls With Bows (O/P) . . 273562
- ❏ Rose (O/P) 273589

Baby Bank

Bookmarks

- ❏ *School Days* Bookmark (O/P) 477346

Candle Huggers

- ❏ Elf Candle Huggers (set/2, O/P) 651419

Candle Toppers

- ❏ Fall Candle Topper 781215

Summer Candle Topper

Candle Toppers, cont.

- ❏ Spring Candle Topper . . 781193
- ❏ Summer Candle Topper . 781207
- ❏ Winter Candle Topper . . 781231

Containers

- ❏ Baby Bank 533319
- ❏ Baby Covered Box 536903
- ❏ Baby With Diaper (covered box, O/P) 203734
- ❏ Bears With Bows (vase, O/P) 203289
- ❏ Blocks Bank (O/P) 203688
- ❏ Easter Basket (3 asst., O/P) 156523
- ❏ Gingerbear Glass Jars (with cork jar toppers,3 asst., O/P) . . 352640
- ❏ Halloween Treat Bag (3 asst., O/P) 141879
- ❏ Heart Shaped Cupid Covered Box (O/P) 111015
- ❏ Heaven Has Blessed This Day (boy, Bible holder) . 345105C
- ❏ Heaven Has Blessed This Day (girl, Bible holder) . 309079C

Bear With Books Age 10

Containers, cont.

- ❏ Heaven Has Blessed This Day (covered box with pendant, O/P) 303216
- ❏ Love Bears All Things (basket, O/P) 203246C
- ❏ Mini Flower Pots With Silk Flowers (3 asst., O/P) . . . 202983
- ❏ Mom – Maker Of Miracles (covered box with necklace, O/P) . 306614
- ❏ Potpourri Holder (O/P). . 537667
- ❏ Stanley and Valerie Covered Box (O/P) 476676
- ❏ Valentine Treat Bags (2 asst., O/P) 156582
- ❏ Victorian With Crochet Covered Box (O/P) 664103
- ❏ Victorian With Love Heart Covered Box (O/P). 664030
- ❏ Victorian With Mirror Covered Box (O/P) 664022

Covered Boxes – Across The Seas

- ❏ American Boy (O/P) . . . 441155
- ❏ Australian Boy (O/P) . . 441031
- ❏ Canadian Boy (O/P) . . . 441058
- ❏ Chinese Boy (O/P). 441066
- ❏ Dutch Girl (O/P) 441090
- ❏ English Boy (O/P) 441139
- ❏ French Girl (O/P) 441074
- ❏ German Boy (O/P) 441082
- ❏ Italian Girl (O/P). 441104
- ❏ Japanese Girl (O/P). . . . 441112
- ❏ Mexican Boy (O/P) 441120
- ❏ Spanish Boy (O/P) 441147

Covered Boxes – Friends To The End

- ❏ Girl Flower 846090
- ❏ Secret Girl 846082

Covered Boxes – Growing Up

- ❏ Baby With Stack Of Blankets 844012
- ❏ Baby With Block 796077
- ❏ Bear With Books 796166
- ❏ Bear With Candy. 796107
- ❏ Bear With Crown. 796115
- ❏ Favors 796123
- ❏ Girl With Birthday Cake . 796093
- ❏ Girl With Bow And Present 796085
- ❏ Ice Cream Dish 796158
- ❏ Slice Of Cake 796131
- ❏ Stack Of Blankets. 796069

Displayers

- ❏ *Across The Seas* Display (O/P). CRT234
- ❏ *Across The Sea* Wood Display (O/P) 281506
- ❏ *Across The Seas* Wreath Display (O/P) 470570
- ❏ *Antique Toy* Christmas Tree Display 707228
- ❏ *Antique Toy* Displayer (O/P). 537640

Slice Of Cake Age 8

Growing Up Box Display

Displayers, cont.

- ❏ *Beta Is For Bears* Easel
  Display (O/P) 306312
- ❏ *Blossoms Of Friendship*
  Display (O/P) CRT228
- ❏ *Bonnets And Bows*
  Gazebo Display (O/P) . . 664669
- ❏ *By the Sea, By The Sea*
  Display (O/P) CRT233
- ❏ *Carousel* Display (O/P) . 545007
- ❏ *Cherished Teddies Friends*
  Collection Attic Displayer
  (O/P) 662062
- ❏ *Childhood Memories*
  Backercard (O/P) 661945
- ❏ *Christmas Carol* Christmas
  Village Backdrop (O/P) . CRT023
- ❏ Christmas Display
  Shadow Box 770043
- ❏ *Count On Me*
  Display (O/P) 302953
- ❏ *Down Strawberry Lane* Picket
  Fence Display (O/P) CRT11
- ❏ *Friends To The End* Easel
  Card Display 862991*
- ❏ *Growing Up* Box
  Display. 823708
- ❏ *Happily Ever After*
  Display (O/P) 302589
- ❏ *Have A Cup Full Of Sweetness*
  Plate Rack Display (O/P) . CRT33
- ❏ *Heart Of Gold* Basket
  Displayer (O/P). 478954
- ❏ *Holiday Dangling*
  Display (O/P) CRT227
- ❏ *Just Between Friends*
  Display (O/P) 362956

Displayers, cont.

- ❏ *Love Letters From*
  Teddie Display (O/P). . . CRT230
- ❏ *Monthly Friends To Cherish*
  Shelf Talker (O/P) CRT089
- ❏ *Monthly Plush*
  Displayer 620297
- ❏ *Nursery Rhyme*
  Displayer (O/P) CRT013
- ❏ *Our Cherished Family*
  House Displayer (O/P) . CRT014
- ❏ *Our Cherished*
  Neighbearhood Fence
  Shelf Display (O/P) 362697
- ❏ *Rainbow Lane*
  Displayer (O/P) CRT026
- ❏ *Santa's Workshop*
  Display (O/P) CRT076
- ❏ *School Days* Basket/
  Backer Display (O/P). . . 478997
- ❏ *Sweetheart Ball*
  Displayer (O/P) CRT096
- ❏ *T Is For Teddies*
  Display CRT101
- ❏ *T-Shirt Teddies* Basket
  Display (O/P) 488585
- ❏ *Teddie Triumphs* Shadow
  Box Display (O/P) 482072
- ❏ *Through The Years*
  Displayer (O/P) CRT004
- ❏ *Tis The Season* Window
  Pane Display (O/P). . CRT182
- ❏ *Tis The Season* Wooden
  Mini Plate Rack
  Display (O/P) 213977
- ❏ Toy Shop Easel
  Backdrop (O/P) CRT002

Cherished Sents Plush Displayer

Tumbling Teddies Display

Displayers, cont.

- ❏ *Tumbling Teddies*
  Display. 662151
- ❏ *Ways To Say I Love You*
  Display. 795941
- ❏ *We Bear Thanks*
  Backdrop (O/P) CRT083
- ❏ *Wet Mittens* Rack
  Displayer 770051
- ❏ *Winter Bear Festival*
  Skating Pond
  Display (O/P) CRT334
- ❏ Wood Shadow Box
  Displayer (O/P) 628557

Drawer Pulls

- ❏ Block Drawer Pull (O/P) . . 203750
- ❏ Cherished Teddie
  Drawer Pull (O/P) 279498

Gift Sets

- ❏ 1999 Mother's Day Gift
  to Go Set (O/P). 605344
- ❏ 2000 Mother's Day Gift
  to Go Set (O/P). 679089
- ❏ Collector Starter Kit. CRT675
- ❏ Computer Kit. 686999

Lamps

- ❏ Bear Holding
  Heart (O/P). 139114
- ❏ Theodore, Samantha
  and Tyler (O/P) 912425

Lamp Shade Toppers

- ❏ Boy On Rocking
  Horse (O/P) 135283
- ❏ Boy Sailor (O/P) 135283
- ❏ Girl With Bonnet (O/P) . . 135283

Light Switch Covers

- ❏ Baby Light Switch Cover . 203661
- ❏ Bear With Bunny Switch
  Plate Cover 853496*

Magnets

- ❏ Boy Sailor (O/P) 902632
- ❏ Boy With Santa
  Cap (O/P) 951234
- ❏ Girl In Stocking (O/P) . . 951234
- ❏ Girl Sailor (O/P) 902632

Miniature Plush

- ❏ Bears With Scented
  Pillows (3 asst.) 842672*

Necklaces and Lockets

- ❏ World's Greatest Mom
  Photo Heart Locket
  (O/P). 476994
- ❏ Heart Of Gold (necklace,
  O/P) 477370

Nightlights

- ❏ Baby Nightlight 536911

Baby Nightlight

Buttons & Bows Buttons

Friends To The End Photo Holders

❑ Just Us Girls 846120*

Ways To Say I Love You Photo Holders

❑ I'll Say It With Chocolates . 790494
❑ I'll Say It With A
Diamond 790478
❑ I'll Say It With A Melody . 790451
❑ I'll Say It With A
Necklace 790443
❑ I'll Say It With A Rose . . 790508
❑ I'll Say It With A Sonnet . 790486

Pins and Earrings

❑ "An Angel To Watch
Over You" (O/P) 176273
❑ "Boo-ti-ful" (O/P) 176230
❑ Blossoms Of Friendship
(4 asst., O/P) 203033
❑ Brown Eyed Susan
❑ Dahlia
❑ Iris
❑ Rose
❑ Buttons & Bows Button
Lapel Pin (3 asst.) 842621*
❑ Easter (O/P) 156574
❑ Follow The Rainbow
(O/P) 310425
❑ Friendship Pin w/Plush . 842613*
❑ Halloween (O/P) 182958
❑ Heart Of Gold (O/P) . . . 477362
❑ Holiday (O/P) 141860
❑ Homecoming Lapel Pin . 759511P*

Pins and Earrings, cont.

❑ "I Love You" Blocks
(pin only, O/P) 203122
❑ Joy Pin w/Plush 842540*
❑ Love (O/P) 156566
❑ "Love" Blocks
(pin only, O/P) 203122
❑ Love Pin w/Plush 842583*
❑ Mom – Maker Of
Miracles (O/P) 303070
❑ St. Patrick's (O/P) 903132
❑ School Days (O/P). 477060
❑ Teddie With Block
Lapel Pin (A-Z, sold
separately, O/P) 203297A-Z
❑ "XO" Blocks
(pin only, O/P) 203122

Stocking Stuffers

❑ Stocking Stuffers
(6 asst., O/P) 354058
❑ bookmark
❑ holiday bear-ette
❑ key chain
❑ magnet
❑ necklace
❑ pin and earrings

Love Lapel Pin

Spotlight on Glenn, The Designer

Since Priscilla Hillman's son, Glenn, started helping out his mom and even designing some pieces of his own, his creativity has been reflected in 22 special pieces. It looks like Glenn's mom might have some competition in the years to come!

Glenn's Portfolio

Calvin

Abraham, *"Your Friendship Means The World To Me"*

Bert, *"I'm Busy As A Bee Every Day Of The Week"*

Billie, *"A Bundle Of Joy From Heaven Above"*

Calvin, *"Life Is Filled With Ups And Downs"*

Cassandra, *"Ghostly Greetings"*

Chad, *"With You My Spirits Soar"*

Chuck, *"You've Always Been A Deere Friend"*

Darren, *"Nothing's Cozier Than Friendship"*

Dave, *"An Oldy But Goodie"*

Dewey, *"Enjoy Your Friends, They're The Refreshments Of Life"*

Glenn, *"By Land Or By Sea, Let's Go – Just You And Me"*

Ken, *"You Make My Heart Race"*

Lance, *"Come Fly With Me"*

"Our Journey Has Just Begun"

Paul Revere, *"You Can Always Trust Me To Be There"*

Ralph, *"Bring Joy To Those You Hold Deer"*

Roger, *"You Set My Heart In Motion"*

Roy, *"I'm Your Country Cowboy"*

Sierra, *"You're My Partner"*

Glenn

Spanky, *"Friendship Can Sometimes Be Bumpy, But It's Worth It"*

Sullivan, *"The Most Important Truth Is To Be True To Yourself"*

Vernon And Eva, *"Wherever Life Takes You, I Won't Be Far Behind"*

Secondary Market Overview

Picture this: you finally have enough time to scoot down to your favorite collectibles store (where they know you by name) and add to your overflowing **Cherished Teddies** collection. When you get there, you spend the afternoon in acquisition, finding those pieces for which you've been looking for years. But there's one piece that – even after you've searched high and low – just isn't in the store. When you ask the friendly salespeople, they tell you that the piece has been retired, and they don't have it in stock. However, just because you can't find it at a retail store doesn't mean that teddie isn't out there somewhere.

"They Broke The Mold When They Made You"

Priscilla Hillman's fertile imagination has been conjuring up new adorable teddies for nearly a decade, and the designs just keep coming. With so many new teddies in the works, Enesco can't keep the old ones around indefinitely, so some pieces must be retired. Each year, Enesco singles out a certain number of pieces and breaks their molds so that the pieces will never be made again. When that happens, the law of supply and demand drives up the retired piece's value, sometimes very highly.

The mold isn't always broken, though. Sometimes Enesco suspends a piece, meaning that although it won't be made for a period of time, the mold will stay intact should they want to make it again. Just like a retired piece, a suspended piece often rises in value. But it could go back on the market at any minute, and the value could go back down as a result.

Some **Cherished Teddies** pieces are only meant to be available for a certain amount of time, or in a limited quantity. Club pieces, for example, are sold during a particular year and are closed at that year's end. Pieces given out at special events, such as collectibles shows, usually aren't sold at any other time in any other place. All of these factors – retirement, suspension, Limited Edition or event pieces – can turn a particular **Cherished Teddies** figurine into a rare and valuable collectible. It may be hard to find, but it can be yours if you know where to look.

Starting Small

One of the best places to start your quest for an elusive teddie is none other than your favorite store. After all, collectors are a social bunch, and stores will often keep tabs on their customers. Perhaps one of the other **Cherished Teddies** collectors will have just the piece you need, and he or she might be willing to sell it or trade for it. The store can also put you in touch with a collectibles exchange, a service which sends you a list of items that its members have for sale. (Some of these exchanges charge a small fee.) And, there are more collectors around than you realize, so don't overlook your local paper. Placing an ad in the classified section may be just what you need to do to find a piece.

Expanding The Net

A collectibles phenomenon like the **Cherished Teddies** collection certainly isn't limited to your own hometown or state. If a local search isn't proving fruitful, you may need to try it on a national level. In days gone by, that would have been a *very* difficult task, but the advent of the Internet has made even worldwide searches a viable option.

When you type "**Cherished Teddies**" or an individual piece's name into a search engine, you'll find hundreds of links, including on-line stores. Just because a retired piece isn't available at one store doesn't mean that it can't be found at *any* store. One of the dealers in cyberspace could very well have the piece you need at a fair price.

But dealers aren't the only people you'll find while surfing the Internet. Many collectors have personal websites devoted to their own collections, and plenty of **Cherished Teddies** fans have found the object of their quest on such a site. After all, what are **Cherished Teddies** collectors, if not a close-knit family? The Internet lets collectors from all over the country meet, trade and talk about their common love for these adorable teddies. Even if you don't find your piece, you'll certainly find a very special community of friends!

Bear In Mind

When you finally find the piece you want, there are several factors that can influence how much you can expect to pay for it. It's not uncommon for collectors to pay too much, or not get paid enough, for a piece they're buying or selling.

Since 1993, each **Cherished Teddies** piece has had a year mark, and that simple stamp affects their value. When you turn a piece over, you'll see a series of numbers that tell you when it was made. For example, a piece made in 1997 will have the number "7" just before the registration, a 1998 piece has an "8," and so forth. Anything made in 2000  has an "I," and the new 2001 pieces are marked "II." If you find a new piece with an older year mark, it might be a spring release, since some spring releases will have the previous year's mark. Just as an 1874 pocket watch is worth more than one made in 1974, older versions of a teddie will usually be more valuable than the newer ones. So, if you're buying or trading a piece, be sure to ask for the year mark before you agree to the deal.

Collectors traditionally take good care of their pieces. Some of them choose to leave them in their original boxes, making for the highly sought after "mint-in-box" condition. But most prefer to show off their acquisitions, and it's almost inevitable that some of them get slightly damaged. The smallest chip or smudge on a piece can drag its value down significantly. The condition of a piece is important to know, especially when you're trading on the Internet. Be sure to ask the seller about the item's condition, or even request a picture of the teddie before you agree to buy it.

The Thrill Of The Chase

Above all, collecting is supposed to be fun, and some collectors find the quest as thrilling as its reward. So, when you're surfing the Net in search of that elusive piece, remember to enjoy yourself! You may find more than you bargained for!

CHERISHED TEDDIES RESOURCES

COLLECTIBLE EXCHANGE, INC.
6621 Columbiana Road
New Middletown, OH 44442
(800) 752-3208/(330) 542-9646
www.colexch.com

DONNA'S COLLECTIBLES EXCHANGE
703 Endeavor Drive South
Winter Springs, FL 32708
1-800-480-5105
www.donnascollexch.com

ENESCO
1-800-NEAR YOU
www.enesco.com

NEW ENGLAND COLLECTIBLES EXCHANGE
Bob Dorman
201 Pine Avenue
Clarksburg, MA 01247
(413) 663-3643
nece@collectiblesbroker.com
www.collectiblesbroker.com

Variations

There's nothing the **Cherished Teddies** bears love more than celebrating their own individuality. Their little color changes, design differences and spelling mistakes can make the value of a variation piece significantly higher than others. However, this is not always true. While it is certain that a variation creates a high interest value, there is no guarantee that it will create a high monetary one. But once again, that is not what collecting is all about. So look closely at your teddies to see if you've got something special!

Fashion Emergency

BETH . . . *"BEAR HUGS"* (#950637) – While bravely riding along, Beth must have gotten her dress dirty, because she's been seen sporting one with green spots, as well as the traditional blue dress. Her horse hasn't been the same old steed either, being seen in both white and tan.

Variation

Standard

CAROL . . . *"ANGELS SNOW HOW TO FLY"* (#352969) – It seems that in some versions of this piece, Carol is sporting blue snow pants instead of her usual red. Maybe the blue ones were too cold to wear while she was making those beautiful snow angels!

JAMES . . . *"GOING MY WAY FOR THE HOLIDAYS"* (#269786) – Maybe James has a twin brother, or a cousin with the same name! He's been spotted going out in the cold not only in a green coat and blue pants, but also in beige pants and red coat.

LOGAN . . . *"LOVE IS A BEAR NECESSITY"* (#103756) – Logan can't seem to decide what he wants to wear in the circus. Some versions have him in blue overalls with a red and yellow tie, while other ones show our little buddy in a red and yellow spotted tie and red overalls. Let's hope he makes up his mind before the show!

WALLY . . . *"YOU'RE THE TOPS WITH ME"* (#103934) – Maybe there was a mix-up in circus wardrobe. Wally has graced the ring in a blue and white suit, but also in a blue and pink suit!

What Are You Saying?

BAILEY AND FRIEND . . . *"THE ONLY THING MORE CONTAGIOUS THAN A COLD IS A BEST FRIEND"* (#662011) – If you take a look at the bottom stamp of this piece, you might see that the folks who stamped it could have used a proofreader!   Some pieces have surfaced that read "Contagions" instead of "Contagious" in the piece's saying.

BILLY . . . *"EVERYONE NEEDS A CUDDLE"* (#624896) – Could it have been fore-shadowing when some of Billy's figurines start-ed showing up with his name spelled Billie? After all, this retired piece got a friend with that name this year!

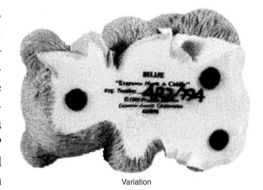

Variation

ELLA . . . *"LOVE GROWS IN MY HEART"* (#156329) – Our intrepid strawberry gal must have been out in the patch too long, because she's had an identity crisis! Some versions of her have Thelma's name and information on the bottom.

JASON . . . *"WHEN IT COMES TO FRIENDSHIP, YOU'VE REALLY EARNED YOUR STRIPES"* (#506214) – The variation which has this piece's underside stamped with "Eamed" instead of "Earned" must have had collectors scratching their heads!

"*A MOTHER'S LOVE BEARS ALL THINGS*" (#624861) – This mother may be patient, but she can't make up her mind what she wants to be called! Some pieces list her saying as "A Mother's Love Bears All Things," while others give it as "A Mum's Love Bears All Things," or even "A Mum Love Bears All Things." It seems that mother's love tolerates honest mistakes, too.

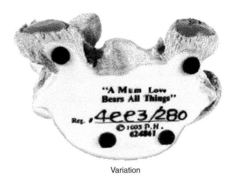

Variation

A New Look

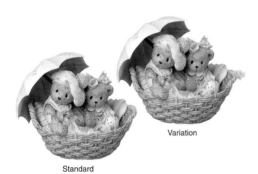

Variation

Standard

BETH AND BLOSSOM . . . "FRIENDS ARE NEVER FAR APART" (#950564) – In some versions of this piece, our two lovely ladies are joined by a colorful butterfly who has landed on their basket's handle.

BILL . . . "FRIENDS LIKE YOU ARE ALWAYS TRUE BLUE" (#505552) – The original prototype of this *Carousel* piece has Bill proudly flying an American flag. Since then, he's switched loyalties, and now waves the honorable **Cherished Teddies** flag instead.

Standard

Variation

FOLLOW THE YELLOW BRICK ROAD COLLECTOR SET (#476501) – Not only does Dot alternate between ruby red slippers and pink ones, in some of the pieces all of the Oz characters are standing in different spots!

Don't Be Fooled

Sometimes, Enesco has issued pieces that are intentionally different from one another. If you think that certain pieces could be variations, be sure to check their item numbers. If the numbers are different, they are totally different pieces. For example, Kent has

Standard   Rare Bear

been known to have a red stop sign, and a green go sign, but these two versions are not the same piece. If you have Miranda in brown, it doesn't mean the original piece just got dirty! Her *Rare Bear* equivalent is white, while her original version is a light brown.

The *Rare Bears* were first released in 1998, and are popular with collectors because these teddies are produced in very limited quantities. How do you know if you have a *Rare Bear*? It all comes down to the bottom stamp; a letter "R" enclosed in a diamond means that the piece is an exclusive *Rare Bear*, not a variation.

Although we've listed several of the variations **Cherished Teddies** collectors might find in their collection, there are still many more out there just waiting to be discovered. The next time you're admiring your darling teddies, pay careful attention – there may be a variation in their midst!

Insuring Your Collection

After all the time and love you have put into your collection, it is important that you make sure it is covered in the event of unforeseen circumstances such as fire or theft. When insuring your collection, there are three major points to consider:

Know Your Coverage — Collectibles are typically included in homeowner's or renter's insurance policies. Ask your agent if your policy covers fire, theft, floods, hurricanes, earthquakes and damage or breakage from routine handling. Also, ask if your policy covers claims at "current replacement value" – the amount it would cost to replace items if they were damaged, lost or stolen – which is extremely important since the secondary market value of some pieces may well exceed their original retail price.

Document Your Collection — In the event of a loss, you will need a record of the contents and value of your collection. Ask your insurance agent what information is acceptable. Keep receipts and an inventory of your collection in a different location, such as a safety deposit box. Include the purchase date, price paid, issue year, edition limit/number, special markings and secondary market value for each piece. Photographs and video footage with close-up views of each piece are good back-ups.

Weigh The Risk — To determine the coverage you need, calculate how much it would cost to replace your collection and compare it to the total amount your current policy would pay. To insure your collection for a specific dollar amount, ask your agent about adding a Personal Articles Floater or a Fine Arts Floater or "rider" to your policy, or even insuring your collection under a totally separate policy. As with all insurance, you must weigh the risk of loss against the cost of additional coverage.

– Key –

*All **Cherished Teddies** resin pieces are listed below in numerical order by stock number. The first number refers to the piece's location within the Value Guide section and the second to the box in which it is pictured on that page. For additional pieces, please see the "Teddies, Teddies Everywhere: Other Products" section on pages 175-179.*

	Pg.	Pic.
CRT025	66	7
CRT064	169	5
CRT065	169	8
CRT109	44	2
CRT122	168	11
CRT124	168	9
CRT240	52	3
CRT279	168	3
CRT289	168	4
CRT442	167	2
CRT466	167	4
CT001	169	6
CT002	169	3
CT003	168	7
CT004	167	6
CT005	166	4
CT007	165	1
CT011	164	4
CT012	164	5
CT013	164	6
CT102	169	2
CT103	168	6
CT104	167	5
CT105	166	5
CT107	164	8
CT205	166	9
CT305	166	8
CT951	169	9
CT952	169	7
CT953	169	4
CT961	169	1
CT962	168	10
CT971	168	5

	Pg.	Pic.
CT972	168	1
CT981	167	7
CT982	167	8
CT983	167	3
CT991	166	11
CT992	166	10
CT993	166	6
CT994	166	2
103551	68	10
103586	38	3
103594	35	7
103608	143	3
103616	143	4
103640		
Be Mine	50	6
Love	50	7
103659		
Boy	60	2
Girl	60	3
103667	61	3
103691	135	5
103713	92	6
103721	93	4
103748	93	6
103756	93	7
103764	53	1
103772	50	4
103780	60	1
103799	47	5
103802	42	1
103810	55	10
103829	62	2
103837	44	4
103845	44	5
103896	58	9
103934	93	10
103942	93	9
103977	92	7
104116		
From	147	10
Heart	148	4
My	149	3
104140		
Charity	147	6
Faith	147	8
Hope	148	10
Love	149	1
104191	133	11
104256	92	8

	Pg.	Pic.
104973	66	2
107700	93	3
110981	147	7
111414	156	7
111430	93	5
114901	152	4
127906	112	3
127914	112	2
127922	111	7
127949	39	2
127957	39	3
127965	58	10
127973	73	10
127981	36	3
128015	69	1
128023		
Christy	45	4
Dorothy	47	8
Millie	62	7
128031	66	6
128031F	66	6
128058	139	6
128066	134	11
128074	134	2
128082	134	12
128104	131	2
128112	134	10
128120	135	1
128902	152	8
131865	59	1
131865F	59	1
131873	48	2
132977	132	7
132993	132	3
135437	152	10
135593	61	1
135682	61	6
135690	62	1
135755	135	4
136166	135	3
136174	135	2
136182	134	5
137596	93	2
139114	137	8
141089	140	8
141100	116	8
141119	117	8
141127	117	7
141135	117	9
141143	118	4

	Pg.	Pic
141178	130	5
141178A	130	6
141186	36	6
141194	59	2
141216	44	3
141224	54	10
141232	142	4
141240	141	1
141259	142	6
141267	108	2
141275	129	2
141283	129	3
141291	129	4
141305	129	1
141313	65	2
141321	43	2
141348	38	4
141542	129	5
141550	151	6
141925	118	3
145033	152	7
151998	152	6
152382	51	7
154016	63	3
155438	56	4
155438A	56	5
156272	67	5
156280	74	7
156299	97	5
156302	97	8
156310	97	7
156329	97	3
156337	97	4
156353	71	10
156353F	71	10
156361	46	8
156388	42	2
156396	59	6
156418	63	1
156426	59	10
156434	121	8
156442	121	7
156450	121	4
156469	121	3
156477	121	5
156485	121	2
156493	151	4
156507	133	1
156515	106	1
156590	150	11

	Pg.	Pic.		Pg.	Pic.		Pg.	Pic.		Pg.	Pic.
156604	... 132	5	176141	... 102	6	203084	... 105	7	239836	... 105	2
158488A	.. 122	2	176168			203114	... 122	1	239844	... 105	3
158488B	.. 122	3	*Ho Ho*	... 101	8	203211	... 147	1	239852	... 105	4
158488C	.. 122	4	*Joy.*	 102	4	203300	 98	8	239860	... 105	5
158488D	.. 122	5	176206	 51	8	203335	 98	7	239933	... 105	6
158488E	.. 122	6	176214	 46	3	203343	 98	6	240281	... 106	3
158488F	.. 122	7	176222	 63	9	203351	 98	5	265780	 46	4
158488G	.. 122	8	176257	 71	7	203386	... 152	1	265780F	... 46	5
158488H	.. 123	1	176265	 36	8	203394	... 152	2	265799	 57	9
158488I	... 123	2	176281	... 150	8	203408	... 151	12	265810	 71	6
158488J	... 123	3	176303	... 150	5	203416	... 152	3	269727	... 130	9
158488K	.. 123	4	176311	... 150	9	203424	 55	2	269735	... 130	7
158488L	.. 123	5	176338	... 150	10	203432	 60	7	269743	... 130	8
158488M	.. 123	6	176346	... 150	6	203440	 59	5	269751	... 129	7
158488N	.. 123	7	176362	... 108	8	203467	 86	5	269778	... 130	1
158488O	.. 123	8	177768	... 142	2	203475	 86	2	269786	... 130	4
158488P	.. 123	9	182966	 64	9	203491	 86	4	269832	 57	1
158488Q	.. 123	10	197254	 77	5	203505	 86	1	269840	 56	6
158488R	.. 124	1	197289	 78	6	203513	 86	3	269859	 55	7
158488S	.. 124	2				203548	 93	1	269891	... 115	7
158488T	.. 124	3	202312	 79	1	203572	 93	8	269905	... 116	2
158488U	.. 124	4	202320	 79	2	203718	... 146	6	269913	... 116	3
158488V	.. 124	5	202339	 77	4	203726	... 151	10	269980	 43	4
158488W	. 124	6	202347	 78	8	203742	... 149	5	269999	 67	1
158488X	.. 124	7	202355	 78	1	203874	 38	1	270016	 38	2
158488Y	.. 124	8	202398	 79	5	203882	... 133	4	272132	... 110	5
158488Z	.. 124	9	202401	 78	4	203920	... 133	3	272140	... 116	7
163457	 38	10	202401P	... 78	5	203939	... 132	6	272159	 71	5
163465	 50	10	202436	 78	2	205354	 37	3	272167	 59	7
163473	 48	1	202436P	... 78	3	215856	 42	5	272175	... 142	9
163481	 69	3	202444P	... 77	3	215864	 64	4	272183	... 151	9
164658	... 152	5	202452	 78	9	215880	 75	9	272361	 64	1
170941	... 152	11	202452P	... 78	10	215910	 73	2	272388	... 110	6
170968	... 152	9	202878	 79	7	216739	 79	3	272426	... 151	11
175560	... 129	6	202878P	... 79	8	216739P	... 79	4	272884	... 130	3
175986	 80	1	202886	 85	3	219061	... 115	8	273198	... 167	10
175994	 80	2	202894	 85	4	219088	... 115	5	273554	... 167	9
176001	 80	3	202908	 84	8	219096	... 116	5	276987	 79	6
176028	 48	7	202932	 84	7	219118.	... 115	6	276995	 77	1
176036	... 116	6	202940	 55	5	219177	... 115	4	276995P	... 77	2
176044	 55	9	202959	 84	9	219312	... 115	9	277002	... 168	8
176052	... 143	9	202959A	... 85	1	219487	... 116	4	279641	... 110	7
176060	... 151	8	202967	 85	2	219525	... 115	3	292494	... 110	8
176079	... 117	3	202991	 97	2	239720	... 104	3	292575	... 130	2
176087	... 102	3	203009	... 150	12	239747	... 104	4	297550	... 168	2
176095	.. 102	1	203017	... 133	2	239763	... 104	5			
176109	... 102	5	203025	... 151	5	239771	... 104	6	302457	... 100	4
176117	... 150	7	203041	 68	3	239798	... 104	7	302465	... 100	3
176125	... 154	2	203068	 48	8	239801	... 104	8	302473	... 100	5
176133	... 102	2	203076	... 106	2	239828	... 105	1	302481	... 100	6

	Pg.	Pic.		Pg.	Pic.		Pg.	Pic.		Pg.	Pic.
302511	... 100	8	306045	 82	6	352616	... 120	5	464112	... 144	8
302570	... 100	7	306053	 82	7	352659	... 113	3	464120	... 143	12
302600	... 128	7	306088	 82	8	352667	... 113	1	466220	 48	3
302619	 68	5	306096	 82	9	352675	... 113	4	466239	... 127	4
302627	 78	7	306118	 83	1	352683	... 113	5	466247	... 127	5
302643	 69	7	306126	 83	2	352691	... 113	2	466255	... 127	6
302651	 51	4	306134	 83	3	352713	... 117	1	466263	... 127	7
302678	 75	3	306142	 83	4	352721	 67	2	466271	 69	5
302686	 41	8	306150	 83	5	352748	... 142	12	466298	 68	1
302694	 46	9	306185	 83	6	352764	... 151	7	466301	 40	4
302708	 35	1	306193	 83	7	352799	 68	9	466328	 65	7
302716	 50	1	306207	 83	8	352950	 50	2	466328I	 65	7
302732	... 121	6	306215	 83	9	352950I	 50	2	475602	 61	4
302759			306223	 83	10	352969	 42	9	476161	 37	6
Key	 76	1	306231	 84	1	352977	 53	2	476285	... 113	7
Locket	 76	2	306258	 84	2	353914	... 131	8	476315	... 113	6
302767	 98	4	306266	 84	3	353922	... 131	7	476323	... 114	2
302775	 98	2	306274	 84	4	353949	... 131	5	476366	... 114	4
302791	 98	1	306282	 84	5	353957	... 131	9	476374	... 114	3
302821	 94	3	306290	 84	6	353965	... 131	4	476382	... 113	8
302848	 94	4	306398	 75	10	353973	... 132	1	476390	 59	3
302856	 94	5	308676	... 128	9	354090	... 142	8	476404	 54	1
302864	 94	6	308684	... 128	8	354104	 53	3	476412	 56	7
302872	 94	7	310409	 98	3	354112	 73	7	476439	 60	5
302899	 94	8	310735	 60	9	354244	 58	6	476463	... 100	9
302902	 95	1	310735A	... 60	10	354252	 41	4	476471	 57	2
302910	 95	2	311588	... 135	12	354260	 69	2	476498	 66	10
302929	 95	3	311596	... 136	1	356255	 62	5	476501	 49	9
302945	 94	2	311618	... 136	2	362417	... 120	7	476528	 81	4
302988	 53	8	311626	... 136	3	366854	 74	5	476528R	... 81	5
303046	... 151	2	311634	... 136	4	366854I	 74	5	476536	 46	10
303054	... 149	2	311642	... 136	5	368156	 35	8	476544	 82	1
303097	... 103	3	311650	... 136	6	368164	 61	7	476560	 81	8
303100	... 103	1	311669	... 136	7	368237	 38	8	476560R	... 81	9
303119	... 103	5	311677	... 136	8	373966	 77	6	476587	 81	7
303127	... 102	8	311707	... 136	9				476595	 99	7
303135	... 103	2	311715	... 136	10	450901	... 144	5	476595R	... 99	8
303143	... 103	4	311723	... 136	11	450928	... 145	2	476617	 67	3
303151	... 103	6	331457	... 138	5	450936	... 144	9	476633	 43	10
303186			331465	... 138	6	450944	... 144	11	476641	 57	7
Boy	 148	5	331473	... 138	2	450952	... 144	10	476668	 68	2
Girl	 148	6	336459	... 139	1	450960	... 144	2	476684	 49	7
303208			336521	 55	3	450979	... 145	1	476692	 58	8
Boy	 148	7	336521I	 55	3	450987	... 144	7	476706	 99	5
Girl	 148	8	337463	 59	4	450995	... 144	3	476706R	... 99	6
305979	 59	8	337579	 66	1	451002	... 144	6	476714	 99	1
305995	 82	2	337579F	... 66	1	451010	... 143	11	476714R	... 99	2
306002	 82	3	352586	... 120	4	451029	... 144	12	476722	 99	3
306010	 82	4	352594	... 120	6	451045	... 144	4	476722R	... 99	4
306037	 82	5	352608	... 121	1	451053	... 144	1	476730	 47	6

Numerical Index

	Pg.	Pic.		Pg.	Pic.		Pg.	Pic.		Pg.	Pic.
476757	72	3	484822	49	3	534161	142	11	589926	87	7
476765	64	6				534188	64	5	589934	87	8
476773	63	5	502898	87	3	534196	151	1	589942	86	9
476781	61	10	503711	63	4	534218	64	2	589942R	87	1
476811	75	5	503738	63	6	534226	62	3	589950	87	2
476838	135	8	505323	162	12	534234	37	2	589969	87	4
476846	74	10	505331	162	11	534242	116	9	589977	86	6
476889	151	3	505358	162	9	534250	70	10	597392	46	2
476897	140	11	505374	162	8	534579	131	3	599352	111	8
476900	140	10	505382	162	13	534587	153	12			
476919	52	5	505390	162	10	534668			601551	69	6
476927	52	4	505498	86	8	hat/scarf.	146	9	601578	43	6
476943			505552	86	7	santa suit.	146	10	601586	67	10
Good Luck.	54	2	505579	87	6	puppy	146	11	601594	69	9
Lucky Charm.	54	3	506206	87	9	536938	138	1	601608	60	6
476951			506214	87	5	537004			601624	71	9
green bow.	132	10	506818	57	5	blue hat.	142	1	601632	72	2
pink bow.	132	11	508659	42	3	green hat.	142	3	601640	49	8
yellow bow.	132	12	510254	114	1	red hat.	142	5	610585	158	8
476978	37	4	510947	71	8	537187	80	5	614777	97	1
477036			510955	68	4	537195	81	1	614785	96	6
Apple.	118	7	510955F	68	4	537209	81	2	614807	96	3
Baseball	118	5	510963	47	1	537217	80	4	617075	72	7
Book	118	6	533297	39	10	537225	81	3	617091	55	8
Pom Poms.	118	8	533300	141	5	537233	80	7	617105	65	3
477044	118	9	533327	146	8	537241	80	6	617113	66	3
477400	125	6	533335	141	8	537268	80	8	617121	75	8
477419	125	5	533343	141	7	537802	131	6	617148	70	9
477427	125	1	533637	39	8	537810	57	8	617156	72	1
477443	125	3	533769	111	1	538299	58	4	617164	75	4
477451	125	2	533777	111	5	538299E	58	4	617172	75	6
477478	125	4	533785	111	6	541222	155	5	617180	41	5
477494	126	1	533793	111	4	542091	53	6	617210	135	6
477508	126	2	533807	111	2	542644	62	9	617229	142	7
477516	126	5	533815	58	5	546526	37	8	617237	53	9
477524	125	9	533823	111	3	546534	56	2	617245	64	3
477559	126	4	533858	56	9	549967	156	1	617253	141	2
477893	50	9	533866	36	5	556165	161	2	617296	96	5
477907	51	1	533874	42	7	556181	161	3	617318	96	7
477915	36	10	533882	67	7	556203	161	4	617326	96	2
481696	101	1	533890	103	8	556246	161	5	622788	96	8
482064			533904	103	7	556270	161	6	622796	48	6
Baby	146	7	533912	103	9	556289	161	7	622818	69	10
Birthday	147	2	534099	52	10	556327	161	8	624772	109	6
Boy	147	4	534102	68	8	556483	161	9	624780	110	1
Bride	147	5	534110	63	8	556688	161	10	624799	110	2
Girl	147	11	534129	52	2	556750	161	11	624802	109	7
Girls	148	2	534137	62	8	556785	161	12	624810	110	4
482544	71	2	534145	51	6	556793	161	13	624829	112	6
482544I	71	2	534153	57	6	556955	166	3	624837	112	9

Numerical Index

	Pg.	Pic.		Pg.	Pic.		Pg.	Pic.		Pg.	Pic.
624845	112	5	644366			662267	162	4	676861	46	5
624853	112	8	boy	155	3	662275	162	3	676888	65	8
624861	112	4	girl	155	4	662291	158	14	676942	81	6
624888	112	1	644382	115	1	662291L	159	1	676985A	114	6
624896			649155			662321	157	14	679089	43	5
Betsey	39	7	Jennifer	157	9	662364	153	3	685747	165	9
Billy	40	1	John	157	11	662372	153	1	685771	165	10
Bobbie	40	2	651095	109	1	662380	153	8	685968	165	5
624918	72	4	651125	112	7	662399	153	4	685976	165	6
624926	139	2	651362	96	4	662402	153	5	686999	72	5
624934	135	7	651370	118	2	662410	153	2	689599G		
625302	138	3	651389	117	4	662453A	114	5	Boy	156	8
625426	118	1	651427	149	6	662437	85	7	Girl	156	9
625434	117	5	651435	139	3	662461	85	6	699314	137	10
625442	117	6	654787	156	4	662496	85	8	699322	137	11
626066	39	9	661597	162	7	662518	85	5	699349	138	10
626074	110	3	661740	120	1	663786	119	5			
627364	134	1	661759	120	3	663794	119	6	706620	42	6
627372			661767	120	2	663808	119	3	706639	64	7
A Friend	147	9	661783	92	5	663824	119	7	706647	67	8
Home	148	9	661791	91	6	663840	119	4	706655	56	3
Live	148	12	661821	92	4	663867	119	8	706663	141	12
Welcome	149	7	661848	91	3	663875	119	9	706698	37	5
627445	139	12	661848S	91	3	663883	119	2	706701	117	2
627453	140	7	661856	92	1	663883A	37	9	706728	54	4
628565	139	7	661864	91	8	663891	119	1	706744	91	4
629618	139	9	661872	92	2	663964	140	9	706760	71	4
629707	75	7	661880	92	3	664111	153	11	706779	43	3
631345	166	7	661899	91	7	666696	158	7	706787	49	4
631736			661910	55	4	666718	45	5	706795	71	1
Jackie	157	8	661929	60	8	666963	60	4	706809	36	9
Karen	157	12	661953	90	9	673986	149	9	706817	90	4
Sara	158	9	661953F	90	9	674001	149	8	706833	41	3
637696	160	11	661996	90	3	674028	150	2	706841	66	9
637939	161	1	662003	90	8	674036	149	10	706868	40	3
637947	160	12	662003F	90	8	674044	150	3	706876	35	3
637955	160	8	662011	90	1	674052	150	1	706892	89	3
637963	160	10	662011F	90	1	674060	149	12	706906	89	6
637971	160	13	662038	90	6	674079	150	4	706930	51	2
637998	160	6	662046	90	7	674087	149	11	706949	75	1
638005	160	9	662046F	90	7	675725	137	4	706957	35	4
638013	160	14	662070	128	2	675733	137	1	706965	91	4
638021	160	7	662089	128	1	675741	137	5	706973	115	2
639206	158	5	662097	128	6	675784	137	2	706981	67	9
644323			662100	128	3	675792	136	12	707007	94	1
green	157	1	662119	128	5	675806	137	6	707031	54	5
purple	157	2	662127	128	4	675814	137	3	707074	139	5
red	157	3	662135	127	9	675822	137	7	707090	140	5
644358	90	2	662240	161	14	676845	73	5	707120	145	6
644358F	90	2	662259	162	2	676853	52	1	707139	145	8

Numerical Index

	Pg.	Pic.		Pg.	Pic.		Pg.	Pic.		Pg.	Pic.
707147	145	5	743801	37	10	789925	159	2	846112	135	11
707155	145	10	745073	54	7	790192	125	8	846309	99	9
707163	145	4	745081	54	6	790206	104	1	846317	100	1
707171	145	3	759511	45	6	790257	162	14	846325	100	2
707198	145	7	770094	160	1	790281	163	2	848522	47	2
707201	145	9	770108	159	14	790303	163	4	848530	53	7
707244	153	6	770116	160	4	790311	163	3	848565	74	9
707252	153	7	770124	160	5	790605	156	10	848573	89	4
707260	152	12	770132	160	3	790613	157	4	848581	89	7
707279	153	9	770140	160	2	790702	158	13	848603	89	8
707295	45	2	770469	75	2	790723	163	1	853623	155	8
707309	44	10	782645	146	2	791349	70	4	864218	37	7
707317	44	6	782653	145	11	791373	70	5	864234	47	10
707325	45	1	782661	146	3	791403	70	3	864242	141	3
707333	44	9	782688	146	5	794406	156	2	864277	42	10
707341	44	8	782718	146	1	797154	47	7	864285	51	5
707368	44	7	784974	46	6	797170	53	5	864293	49	2
707384	148	1	785326	140	4	798479	157	13	864307	70	1
707392	147	3	785334	140	6	798487	156	14	864315	41	7
707406	146	4	786578	62	10	798827	155	11	864366	73	8
708437	165	3	786586	65	1	798835	35	5	864374	104	2
708437K	165	4	786683	90	10				865001	143	10
708569	159	6	786691	90	5	805564	69	4	865036	89	5
708593	159	7	786705	74	8	805572	61	9	865044	143	8
708615	159	8	786837	38	6	805580	49	1	865079	154	3
708623	159	9	786845	47	4	805610	57	3	865087	38	5
708631	159	10	786861	114	7	811734	102	7	865095	72	6
708658	159	11	787752	139	10	811742	79	9	865133	143	2
708666	159	12	789577	36	4	811971	157	7	866032	158	10
708674	159	13	789585	45	10	819727	45	8	866040	158	12
721174	44	1	789615	67	6	822353	64	8	866059	155	1
726621	56	8	789623	48	9	823295	53	10	866067	159	4
726664	148	11	789631	65	6	824291	164	7	867268	157	10
726702	35	6	789658	47	3	824305	164	3	867276	158	11
726737	73	9	789666	55	1	824313	164	1	867284	156	6
726745	155	10	789674	95	7	824313C	164	2	867292	157	5
726753	159	5	789682	95	5	833274	101	4	867470	48	4
731765	166	1	789690	95	9	833282	101	6	867489	49	6
731870	41	9	789704	96	1	833290	101	2	869074		
737380	162	6	789712	95	8	833304	41	2	*From*	40	7
737399	162	1	789720	95	4	833312	40	10	*Sealed*	40	8
738638	74	1	789739	95	6	833320	101	7	869082		
739022	53	4	789828	126	6	833401	50	8	*Heart*	40	5
739049	46	7	789836	125	7	833428	40	9	*My Love*	40	6
741094			789844	126	3	833436	41	1	873438	42	8
Groom	91	1	789879	70	2	833444	65	10	873446	158	6
Taught	91	2	789887	132	4	833983	101	5	874671	58	1
742740	162	5	789895	132	8	833991	101	3	874728	65	9
742961	59	9	789909	132	2	846074	135	10	881775	155	9
742988	69	8	789917	132	9	846104	135	9	882119	159	3

Numerical Index

	Pg.	Pic.
882178	148	3
882208	134	9
888036	155	6
888044	155	7
888737	157	6
888753	156	5
900354	138	7
900362	35	2
900931	97	6
902772		
Boy Sailor	133	9
Girl Sailor	134	6
902950	105	8
902969	105	9
903337	138	12
903485	108	6
903620	36	1
903779	140	2
904309	108	9
904546	139	4
906530	131	1
906700		
Boy	133	12
Girl	134	3
910651	46	1
910678	43	7
910686	52	7
910694	43	9
910708	52	6
910724	66	4
910732	36	7
910740	73	4
910759	63	2
910767	61	5
910775	62	4
910783		
Boy	133	10
Girl	134	8
910791	133	6
911283	127	3
911291	127	2
911305	127	1
911313	126	9
911321	126	8
911348	126	7
911356	127	8
911372	73	6
911402	67	4
911410	65	5

	Pg.	Pic.
911429	65	4
911704	133	7
911712	134	4
911720	133	8
911739		
Harrison	51	10
Jonathan	56	10
Thomas	73	3
911747	50	3
912425	137	9
912751	62	6
912778	51	3
912786	50	5
912794	45	7
912808	66	8
912816		
Brenda	41	6
Buckey	41	10
912832	143	1
912840	61	8
912859	138	11
912867	109	2
912875	36	2
912883	72	8
912891	142	10
912905	109	3
912921	43	1
912956	51	9
912964	138	8
912980		
Bells	107	7
Harp	107	8
Trumpet	107	9
912999		
Bear	133	5
Girl	134	7
913006	141	6
913014	141	4
913855	154	1
914304	138	9
914312	139	11
914320	137	12
914746	108	5
914754	106	7
914762	107	5
914770	107	1
914789	106	4
914797	107	2
914800	106	9
914819	106	8

	Pg.	Pic.
914827	106	5
914835	107	6
914843	107	4
914851	107	3
914878	106	6
914894	141	9
914975	156	11
914983	156	12
914991	156	13
916277	48	5
916285	52	9
916293	74	6
916307	58	7
916315	63	7
916323	140	1
916331	38	7
916358		
Bonnet	70	6
Hat	70	8
Headband	70	7
916382		
Hugs	74	2
Love	74	3
Purr-fect	74	4
916390	45	9
916404	39	1
916412	49	5
916420	52	8
916439	68	7
916447	58	2
916641	64	10
916684	108	7
916692	158	1
916706	158	2
916714	158	3
916730	158	4
935557	116	1
950424	42	4
950432		
Jacki	54	8
Karen	57	10
Sara	68	6
950440	58	3
950459	37	1
950475	55	6
950483	45	3
950491	76	3
950505	72	9
950513	63	10
950521	56	1

	Pg.	Pic.
950548	38	9
950556	57	4
950564	39	6
950572	61	2
950637	39	4
950645	140	3
950653	141	10
950661	47	9
950688	108	4
950718	109	5
950726	109	4
950734	54	9
950742	43	8
950769	72	10
950777	140	12
950785	138	4
950793	141	11
950807	39	5
950815	139	8
951005	149	4
951129	71	3
951137	108	1
951196	73	1
951218	108	3
951226		
Boots	143	5
Bow	143	6
Scarf	143	7

– Key –

All **Cherished Teddies** resin pieces are listed below in alphabetical order. The first number refers to the piece's location within the Value Guide section and the second to the box in which it is pictured on that page. For additional pieces, see the "Teddies, Teddies Everywhere: Other Products" section on pages 175--179.

	Pg.	Pic.
4th Of July	160	6
25 Years To Treasure Together	35	1
1999 Membears Only Float	166	2
2000 Membearship Lapel Pin (#708437)	165	3
2000 Membearship Lapel Pin (#708437K)	165	4
2001 Membearship Lapel Pin (#824313)	164	1
2001 Membearship Lapel Pin (#824313C)	164	2
Abigail	35	2
Abraham	35	3
Absence Makes Friendships Grow Stronger	35	4
Adam	129	7
Adelaide	35	5
Agatha	35	6
Age 1	126	7
Age 2	126	8
Age 3	126	9
Age 4	127	1
Age 5	127	2
Age 6	127	3
Age 7	127	4
Age 8	127	5
Age 9	127	6
Age 10	127	7
Aiming For Your Heart	35	7
Alan	106	4
Albert And Susann	91	3
Alex	35	8
Alice (#903620)	36	1
Alice (#912875)	36	2
Alicia	100	3
Allison & Alexandria	36	3
Alma And Austin	36	4
Alyssa	36	5
Amanda	36	6
Amelia	167	9
American Boy (ornament)	143	11
American Boy (plush)	159	6
Amy	36	7
Andre	125	7
Andy	36	8
Angel	140	12
Angel In Red Coat	150	5
Angel On Bell	131	1
Angel With Bells	107	7
Angel With Harp	107	8
Angel With Trumpet	107	9
Angela (#175986)	80	1
Angela (#706809)	36	9
Angelo Bearcino	164	3

	Pg.	Pic.
Angie	108	1
Anita	36	10
Anna	37	1
Anne	37	2
Annette	111	1
Annie, Brittany, Colby, Danny and Ernie	37	3
Anthony (#476528)	81	4
Anthony (#476528R)	81	5
Anxiously Awaiting The Arrival	37	4
April	88	4
April (plush)	161	5
Archie	86	6
Ariel	37	5
Arnold	37	6
Arthur	106	5
Astrid	37	7
Audrey D. Zeiner	165	5
August	88	8
August (plush)	161	9
Australian Boy	143	12
Autumn	152	12
Autumn Brings A Season Of Thanksgiving	151	12
Autumn Outfit	155	1
Ava	37	8
Ava (plush)	155	2
Avon Millennium Exclusive	37	9
Awaiting The Arrival	37	10
Awesome!	125	1
Baby	127	8
Baby (frame, #203920)	133	4
Baby (plaque)	146	6
Baby & Me	133	5
Baby Angel	149	8
Baby Angel On Cloud	141	1
Baby Boy	111	7
Baby Boy (musical)	137	9
Baby Cradle	137	1
Baby Girl	111	8
Baby Girl (musical)	137	10
Baby Girl With Lamb	146	7
Baby In Basket	141	2
Baby In Blanket	141	3
Baby In Cradle	137	11
Baby Plush (boy)	155	3
Baby Plush (girl)	155	4
Baby With Diaper Shelf Sitter	38	1
Baby's 1st Christmas (musical)	138	1
Baby's 1st Christmas (plaque)	146	8
Baby's 1st Christmas Photo Frame Ornament	141	5
Baby's 1st Christmas Rattle Ornament	141	7
Baby's 1st Christmas Spoon Ornament	141	8
Baby's First Christmas (ornament, #913006)	141	6
Baby's First Christmas (ornament, #913014)	141	4
Baby's First Christmas (plaque)	150	6
Bailey And Friend	90	1
Balcony Display	122	1
Ballerina	137	2
Barbara	129	1
Barry	38	2
Baseball	162	14
Basketball	163	1
Baxter	90	2

	Pg.	Pic.
Bazza (#276995)	77	1
Bazza (#276995P)	77	2
Be My Bow	38	3
Bea	38	4
Bear Ballerina	138	2
Bear Cratchit	96	2
Bear In Bunny Hat	138	3
Bear In Cart	145	3
Bear In Hat And Scarf	146	9
Bear In Sail Boat (ornament)	145	4
Bear In Sail Boat (plush)	162	6
Bear In Santa Cap	141	9
Bear In Santa Suit	146	10
Bear In Stocking	141	10
Bear In Stocking Cap	138	4
Bear In Teacup	138	5
Bear In Train	138	6
Bear Mermaid	38	5
Bear Mermaid (waterglobe)	154	3
Bear On Bear	161	14
Bear On Bunny (ornament)	145	5
Bear On Bunny (plush)	162	1
Bear On Cow (ornament)	145	6
Bear On Cow (plush)	162	2
Bear On Elephant (ornament)	145	7
Bear On Elephant (plush)	162	3
Bear On Horse (ornament)	145	8
Bear On Horse (plush)	162	4
Bear On Lamb (ornament)	145	9
Bear On Lamb (plush)	162	5
Bear On Rocking Reindeer (ornament)	141	11
Bear On Rocking Reindeer (waterdome)	138	7
Bear On Teddie	145	10
Bear Sitting Candleholder	131	3
Bear Sitting On Moon	141	12
Bear w/Red Heart	155	5
Bear With 0 Block	94	2
Bear With 1 Block	94	3
Bear With 2 Block	94	4
Bear With 3 Block	94	5
Bear With 4 Block	94	6
Bear With 5 Block	94	7
Bear With 6 Block	94	8
Bear With 7 Block	95	1
Bear With 8 Block	95	2
Bear With 9 Block	95	3
Bear With A Block	122	2
Bear With April Birthstone	104	6
Bear With April Birthstone (frame)	136	4
Bear With August Birthstone	105	2
Bear With August Birthstone (frame)	136	8
Bear With B Block	122	3
Bear With Banner	102	8
Bear With Blue Hat/Scarf	142	1
Bear With Books And Crayon	103	1
Bear With C Block	122	4
Bear With Christmas Mug	155	6
Bear With D Block	122	5
Bear With Dangling Mittens	142	2
Bear With December Birthstone	105	6
Bear With December Birthstone (frame)	136	12
Bear With E Block	122	6
Bear With F Block	122	7
Bear With February Birthstone	104	4
Bear With February Birthstone (frame)	136	2
Bear With G Block	122	8
Bear With Green Hat/Scarf	142	3
Bear With H Block	123	1
Bear With Holly Mug	155	7
Bear With I Block	123	2
Bear With Ice Skates	142	4
Bear With J Block	123	3
Bear With January Birthstone	104	3
Bear With January Birthstone (frame)	136	1
Bear With July Birthstone	105	1
Bear With July Birthstone (frame)	136	7
Bear With June Birthstone	104	8
Bear With June Birthstone (frame)	136	6
Bear With K Block	123	4
Bear With L Block	123	5
Bear With Lunch Box	155	8
Bear With M Block	123	6
Bear With March Birthstone	104	5
Bear With March Birthstone (frame)	136	3
Bear With May Birthstone	104	7
Bear With May Birthstone (frame)	136	5
Bear With N Block	123	7
Bear With November Birthstone	105	5
Bear With November Birthstone (frame)	136	11
Bear With O Block	123	8
Bear With October Birthstone	105	4
Bear With October Birthstone (frame)	136	10
Bear With P Block	123	9
Bear With Paint And Brush	103	2
Bear With Pillow	103	3
Bear With Puppy	146	11
Bear With Q Block	123	10
Bear With R Block	124	1
Bear With Red Hat/Scarf	142	5
Bear With S Block	124	2
Bear With Scarf	133	6
Bear With Scroll	103	4
Bear With September Birthstone	105	3
Bear With September Birthstone (frame)	136	9
Bear With Sign	103	5
Bear With T Block	124	3
Bear With Toy Train	138	8
Bear With U Block	124	4
Bear With V Block	124	5
Bear With W Block	124	6
Bear With Winter Mug	155	9
Bear With X Block	124	7
Bear With Y Block	124	8
Bear With Z Block	124	9
Bearing Easter Blessings	155	10
Bears With Double Hearts	147	1
Beary Special Groom-To-Be, A	113	6
Beatrice	38	6
Beatrice (plush)	155	11
Beautiful And Bearly Blushing	113	7
Becky	38	7
Benjamin	38	8
Benji	38	9
Benny	167	10
Bernard and Bernice Beary	168	1
Bert	125	8
Bertie	38	10
Bessie	39	1
Best Friends	101	2

	Pg.	Pic.
Best Friends (frame)	135	10
Best Friends (plush)	162	8
Best Is Yet To Come, The (#127949)	39	2
Best Is Yet To Come, The (#127957)	39	3
Beth (#950637)	39	4
Beth (#950807)	39	5
Beth And Blossom	39	6
Betsey	39	7
Bette	39	8
Betty	39	9
Bianca	39	10
Big Hug From A Little Friend, A	80	4
Bill	86	7
Billie	104	1
Billy	40	1
Birthday Bear	147	2
Blaire Beary	168	2
Blue Bear With Ribbon	156	1
Blue Mitten	145	11
Bob	77	3
Bobbie	40	2
Bobby	40	3
Bonnie And Harold	40	4
Booker And Fletcher	114	7
Boy And Girl (#910791)	133	7
Boy And Girl (#911704)	133	8
Boy And Girl Cupid, *Heart To Heart*	40	5
Boy And Girl Cupid, *My Love*	40	6
Boy And Girl With Banner	142	6
Boy And Girl With Mittens	147	4
Boy Cupid, *From My Heart*	40	7
Boy Cupid, *Sealed With Love*	40	8
Boy Dressed As Clown	149	9
Boy Golfing	137	3
Boy Graduate	147	4
Boy Hugging Girl	149	10
Boy Praying (frame)	133	9
Boy Praying (musical)	138	9
Boy Prince	110	6
Boy Raking Leaves	149	11
Boy Sailor	133	10
Boy With Barrel	131	4
Boy With Books And Apple	40	9
Boy With Cat	133	11
Boy With Holly	153	12
Boy With Horse Shoe	40	10
Boy With Puppy	133	12
Boy With Santa Cap	134	1
Boy With Scarf	154	1
Boy With Suitcases	41	1
Boy With Thank You Card	41	2
Boy With Toys	149	12
Boy With Trunk	131	5
Brad Wheeler as Troy "Mac" McBear	165	6
Bradley	41	3
Brandon	41	4
Breanna	41	5
Brenda	41	6
Brenna	41	7
Brett	100	4
Brian	111	2
Bride And Groom (invitation holder)	134	2
Bride And Groom (musical)	138	10
Bride And Groom (plaque)	147	5
Bridesmaid	137	4
Brooke	41	8
Bruno	92	6
Bryce	41	9
Bubbie Waterton	167	1
Buckey	41	10
Buddy	89	3
Buddy (plush)	156	2
Bunny	42	1
Butch	42	2
Caleb And Friends	90	3
Calvin	91	4
Cameron	42	3
Camille	42	4
Can't Bear To See You Under The Weather	42	5
Canadian Boy	144	1
Canadian Exclusive Bear	156	3
Candace	130	1
Carla	42	6
Carlin & Janay	42	7
Carlos	77	4
Carlton	42	8
Carol	42	9
Caroline	42	10
Carolyn	43	1
Carrie	43	2
Carter and Elsie	98	1
Carter And Friends	90	4
Casey	115	3
Cassandra	43	3
Cathy	43	4
Cecilia	43	5
Celeste	108	2
Chad	125	9
Chantel And Fawn	120	1
Charissa & Ashylynn	43	6
Charity	43	7
Charity (plaque)	147	6
Charlie	43	8
Cheerleader	163	2
Chelsea	43	9
Cherish	43	10
Cherish The King	138	11
Cherish This Birthday Forever	44	1
Cherished Irish Blessing, A	147	7
Cherished Teddies Club "Bear Tag" Necklace	167	2
Cherished Teddies Club Membearship Pin (#CRT124)	168	9
Cherished Teddies Club Membearship Pin (#CRT279)	168	3
Cherished Teddies In Sleigh	142	7
Cherished Teddies Town Accessory Set	167	3
Cherished Teddies Town Backdrop	169	5
Cherished Teddies Town Depot Easel	168	4
Cherished Teddies Town Sign	44	2
Cherished Teddies Town Teddie Care Center/Ambulance Easel Display	167	4
Cheryl and Carl	44	3
Chinese Boy	144	2
Christian	44	4
Christina	100	5
Christine	44	5
Christmas	160	7

	Pg.	Pic.
Christmas Advent Calendar	142	8
Christmas Bear (musical)	138	12
Christmas Bear (plush)	156	4
Christmas Bear Gift Bag	156	5
Christmas Decorated House	113	1
Christmas Ghosts	96	3
Christmas Mini Figurine, *Boy With Overalls And Santa Hat*	44	6
Christmas Mini Figurines, *Christmas Tree Accessory*	44	7
Christmas Mini Figurine, *Dad Holding Hanging Ornament*	44	8
Christmas Mini Figurine, *Girl With Bowl And Spoon*	44	9
Christmas Mini Figurine, *Girl With Gingerbread Doll*	44	10
Christmas Mini Figurine, *Girl Wrapping Gift*	45	1
Christmas Mini Figurine, *Santa Boy Sitting With Toy*	45	2
Christmas Mini Figurines	117	3
Christmas Tealight Candleholder	131	6
Christmas Tree Plush	156	6
Christopher	45	3
Christy	45	4
Chuck	102	7
Cindy	115	4
Circle Of Love	45	5
Circus Elephant With Bear	92	7
Circus Gift Set	92	8
Circus Lion	93	1
Circus Seal With Ball	93	2
Circus Tent With Rings	93	3
Clara	110	6
Claudette	77	5
Claudia	93	4
Clement And Jodie	91	5
Clown Bear	156	7
Clown On Ball (#111430)	93	5
Clown On Ball (#336459)	139	1
Cody	86	8
Cole (#476714)	99	1
Cole (#476714R)	99	2
Colin	115	5
Collectible Print of Julia Bearon with Bookmark	165	7
Collecting Cherished Friends Along The Way	45	6
Colleen	77	6
Collette	85	5
Communion	119	1
Congratulations (#477451)	125	2
Congratulations (#663883)	119	2
Connie	45	7
Constable Mackenzie	45	8
Corey	81	6
Country Charm	153	1
Country Christmas Accessories	111	3
Couple In Laundry Basket	139	2
Couple In Sleigh	139	3
Courtney	45	9
Craig and Cheri	121	2
Cratchit's House, The (night light)	96	4
Cream Mitten	146	1
Creche With Coverlet	108	3
Crystal (#589942)	86	9
Crystal (#589942R)	87	1
Cub E. Bear	169	6
Cynthia, Ethel, Nanette, Lola, Opal & Janel	45	10
Dad, Drake And Dustee	91	6
Daddy And Me	134	3
Dahlia	84	7
Daisy	46	1
Daisy & Chelsea	46	2
Dangling Snow Flake	142	9
Daniel	46	3
Danielle, Sabrina, Tiffany	46	4
Danny	46	5
Daphne	120	2
Darla	121	3
Darrel	121	4
Darren	46	6
Dave	126	1
Dawn (#661899)	91	7
Dawn (#739049)	46	7
Debbie	46	8
Decade Of Teddy Bear Love, A	46	9
December	89	2
December (plush)	161	13
Deena Wilde	164	4
Delia	46	10
Delight	89	4
Denise	106	6
Dennis	47	1
Dennis And Barb	47	2
Destiny And Kay	47	3
Dewey	94	1
Diana	47	4
Diane	97	2
Diaper Bear (boy)	156	8
Diaper Bear (girl)	156	9
Dina	129	2
Donald	47	5
Donna	47	6
Doris	47	7
Doris (plush)	156	10
Dorothy	47	8
Dot	49	9
Douglas	47	9
Dr. Darlene Makebetter (#CT004)	167	7
Dr. Darlene Makebetter (#CT104)	167	5
Drew	47	10
Drummer Boy	142	10
Dudley	93	6
Duncan	48	1
Dustin and Austin	126	2
Dutch Girl	144	3
Dutch Girl (plush)	159	7
Earl	48	2
Easter (egg, #156507)	133	2
Easter (egg, #203017)	133	3
Easter (plate, #156590)	150	11
Easter (plate, #203009)	150	12
Easter (plush)	160	8
Easter Egg Tea Set	153	1

	Pg.	Pic.
Easter Eggs		
Egg With Green Bow	132	11
Egg With Pink Bow	132	12
Egg With Yellow Bow	133	1
Ebearnezer Scrooge	96	5
Ed	48	3
Edna	48	4
Edward With Donkey	109	5
Eleanor P. Beary	168	5
Elf Riding Candy Cane	117	4
Elf With Doll	117	5
Elf With Stuffed Reindeer	117	6
Elizabeth & Ashley	48	5
Ella	97	3
Ellen	98	2
Elmer And Friends	90	5
Elsa (#914975)	156	11
Elsa (#914983)	156	12
Elsa (#914991)	156	13
Emily E. Claire	168	10
Emma	103	7
English Boy	144	4
Eric	48	6
Erica	48	7
Erika	89	5
Erin	48	8
Ernest And Bugsy	91	8
Ernestine And Regina	48	9
Eskimo Holding Fish	142	11
Eskimos Holding Stars	151	1
Esther	49	1
Ethan	49	2
Evan	49	3
Eve	49	4
Everyone Needs An Occasional Hug	80	5
Exclusive 5th Anniversary		
Mini Figurine	166	3
Expectant Mom	137	5
Faith	49	5
Faith (plaque)	147	8
Family On Toboggan	139	4
Father	112	1
Fay	49	6
Fay & Arlene	49	7
February	88	2
February (plush)	161	3
Felicia	103	8
Felix	49	8
Fernando	78	1
Festival Boy Musical Waterglobe	130	2
Festival Girl Musical Waterglobe	130	3
Flossie	87	2
Follow The Rainbow Mini Accessories	98	3
Follow The Yellow Brick Road		
Collector Set	49	9
Follow Your Heart		
Wherever It Takes You	80	6
Football	163	3
Forever Yours, Forever True	50	1
Frances	95	4
Frank And Helen	50	2
Franz (#202436)	78	2
Franz (#202436P)	78	3
Fred	92	1

	Pg.	Pic.
Freda And Tina	50	3
French Girl	144	5
Friend Is A Treasure Of The Heart, A	147	9
Friend Is An Answered Prayer, A	80	7
Friends To The End	135	11
From My Heart	147	10
Frosty And Aurora	156	14
Functional Nutcracker	110	5
Gabriel	96	3
Gail	50	4
Garland	96	3
Gary	50	5
German Boy	144	6
German Boy (plush)	159	8
Giacomo "Jake" Bearcino	164	5
Gina	87	3
Ginger	117	7
Gingerbread Bear	142	12
Girl And Boy With Kite	147	11
Girl Cupid, *Be Mine.*	50	6
Girl Cupid, *Love.*	50	7
Girl In Red Coat	150	7
Girl In Stocking	134	4
Girl On Carousel	139	5
Girl On Ottoman	139	6
Girl On Rocking Horse	139	7
Girl On Rocking Reindeer (#629618)	139	9
Girl On Rocking Reindeer (#950815)	139	8
Girl On Unicorn	139	10
Girl Praying (frame)	134	5
Girl Praying (musical)	139	11
Girl Reading With Doll	134	6
Girl Sailor	134	7
Girl Standing	99	9
Girl With Basket	131	7
Girl With Blanket	131	8
Girl With Christmas Ribbon (green)	157	1
Girl With Christmas Ribbon (purple)	157	2
Girl With Christmas Ribbon (red)	157	3
Girl With Christmas Wreath	148	1
Girl With Doll	134	8
Girl With Goose	139	12
Girl With Green Coat	150	8
Girl With Heart Harp	140	1
Girl With Hearts	134	9
Girl With Muff (musical)	140	2
Girl With Muff (ornament)	143	1
Girl With Pinecones	131	9
Girl With Roller Skate	150	1
Girl With Scarf	154	2
Girl With Stethescope	50	8
Girl With Tree Trunk	132	1
Girls In Basket With Umbrella	140	3
Girls With Teddies And Cookies	148	2
Glenn	50	9
Gloria	96	3
Good Job	125	3
Gordon	50	10
Grace	80	2
Graduation (#477907)	51	1
Graduation (#663808)	119	3
Grandma	112	2
Grandpa	112	3

	Pg.	Pic.
Great Friendships Make A Solider Stand Tall	51	2
Greek Alpha Bear	82	2
Greek Beta Bear	82	3
Greek Chi Bear	84	4
Greek Delta Bear	82	5
Greek Epsilon Bear	82	6
Greek Eta Bear	82	8
Greek Gamma Bear	82	4
Greek Iota Bear	83	1
Greek Kappa Bear	83	2
Greek Lambda Bear	83	3
Greek Mu Bear	83	4
Greek Nu Bear	83	5
Greek Omega Bear	84	6
Greek Omicron Bear	83	7
Greek Phi Bear	84	3
Greek Pi Bear	83	8
Greek Psi Bear	84	5
Greek Rho Bear	83	9
Greek Sigma Bear	83	10
Greek Tau Bear	84	1
Greek Theta Bear	82	9
Greek Upsilon Bear	84	2
Greek Xi Bear	83	6
Greek Zeta Bear	82	7
Green Mitten	146	2
Gregg	86	1
Gretchen	98	5
Gretel	51	3
Growing Better Each Year	51	4
Grumps	157	4
Guy	51	5
Haley and Logan	51	6
Halloween	160	9
Halloween House	51	7
Halloween Mini Figurines	51	8
Hanging Ornament Plush	157	5
Hannah	98	6
Hans	51	9
Happiness	127	9
Happy Anniversary	119	4
Happy Birthday (#662410)	153	2
Happy Birthday (#663786)	119	5
Harriet	81	7
Harrison	51	10
Harry	121	6
Hartford Printing Co., Firehouse #1 And The Honey Buns Shop Backdrop	168	11
Harvest Small Plaque	148	3
Harvest Square Picture Frame	134	10
Harvey	52	1
Harvey and Gigi	100	6
Hazel	52	2
Heart Dangling Blocks	105	7
Heart To Heart	52	3
Heart To Heart (plaque)	148	4
Heather And Friends	90	6
Heaven Has Blessed This Day (cross plaque, boy)	148	7
Heaven Has Blessed This Day (cross plaque, girl)	148	8
Heaven Has Blessed This Day (Avon figurine, boy)	52	4
Heaven Has Blessed This Day (Avon figurine, girl)	52	5
Heaven Has Blessed This Day (plaque, boy)	148	5
Heaven Has Blessed This Day (plaque, girl)	148	6
Heidi And David	52	6
Henrietta	52	7
Henry	52	8
Herr Drosselmeyer	110	6
Hilary Hugabear	169	7
Ho Ho Blocks	101	8
Holden	102	1
Holding On To Someone Special	52	9
Holly	117	8
Holly Bear Gift Bag	157	6
Home Is Where The Heart Is	148	9
Homecoming Collector Plush	157	7
Homer And Friends	90	7
Honey	52	10
Hope	53	1
Hope (plaque)	148	10
Howard	126	3
Hug Me	162	9
Humphrey	53	2
Hunter	53	3
Hurray It's Your Birthday	53	4
I Just Called To Say I Love You	53	5
I Love Bears Letters	105	8
I Love Hugs	53	6
I Love Hugs Letters	105	9
I Love You	101	3
I Love You Letters	106	1
I Need You	162	10
I Said An Easter Prayer	148	11
I'll Be Counting The Minutes 'Til We Meet Again	132	3
I'm A Beary Lucky Groom	91	1
I'm Proud Of You	125	4
I've Got The Most Important Job!	113	8
Icabod	53	7
If A Mom's Love Comes In All Sizes, Yours Has The Biggest Of Hearts	53	8
Indian Girl	144	7
Indian Girl (plush)	159	9
Ingrid	53	9
Inspector Yukon	53	10
Irene	54	1
Iris	84	7
Irish Girl	137	6
Irish Girl (plush)	159	10
Irish Mini Figurine, Good Luck	54	2
Irish Mini Figurine, Lucky Charm	54	3
Irmgard	54	4
Isaac, Jeremiah & Temperance	54	5
It's A Boy	54	6
It's A Girl	54	7
Italian Girl	144	8
Italian Girl (plush)	159	11
Ivan	87	4
Ivory	159	14
Jack	106	7
Jack & Jill	109	6

	Pg.	Pic.
Jack and Jill (bookends)	131	2
Jack and Jill (clock)	132	4
Jack and Jill (frame)	134	11
Jack and Jill (plate)	152	4
Jacki	54	8
Jackie	157	8
Jacob	54	9
Jacob Bearly	96	6
James	130	4
Jamie And Ashley	54	10
Jan And Elise	55	1
Jane	55	2
Janet	55	3
Janice	55	4
January	88	1
January (plush)	161	2
Japanese Girl	144	9
Jasmine (#202940)	55	5
Jasmine (#950475)	55	6
Jasmine (plush)	160	1
Jason	87	5
Jean	55	7
Jedediah	55	8
Jeffrey	55	9
Jenelle	87	6
Jenna	97	4
Jennifer	55	10
Jennifer (plush)	157	9
Jerald And Mary Ann	79	9
Jeremy	56	1
Jerome	56	2
Jerrod	87	7
Jerry	86	2
Jesse	56	3
Jessica (#155438)	56	4
Jessica (#155438A)	56	5
Jilly	121	5
Jim And Joey	86	3
Jingle Bell Plush	157	10
Joan	143	2
Joann	56	6
Joe	56	7
Joey And Lindsey	56	8
John	129	3
John (plush)	157	11
John And William	56	9
Jolene	102	2
Jonathan	56	10
Jordan	57	1
Joseph	57	2
Josette	57	3
Joshua	57	4
Journey With You Is One To Remember, A	80	8
Joy	102	3
Joy Blocks	102	4
Joyce	98	4
Jude	57	5
Judy	86	4
Julia Bearon as Gloria Growlette (with black dog)	165	8
Julia Bearon as Gloria Growlette (with white dog)	165	9
Julie	106	8
Juliet	122	1
July	88	7
July (plush)	161	8
June	106	9
June (Avon)	88	6
June (plush)	161	7
June And Jean	57	6
Junior	57	7
Just Us Girls	135	12
Justin	111	4
Justine And Janice	57	8
Kaitlyn	128	7
Kara	57	9
Karen	57	10
Karen (plush)	157	12
Katherine (#302732)	121	6
Katherine (#874671)	58	1
Kathleen	58	2
Katie	58	3
Katie, Renee, Jessica, Matthew	58	4
Katrien (#202401)	78	4
Katrien (#202401P)	78	5
Kayla	58	5
Keep Good Friends Close To Your Heart	81	1
Keep Trying	125	5
Keith and Deborah	58	6
Kelly	58	7
Kelsie	100	7
Ken	126	4
Kendra	58	8
Kent (#476560)	81	8
Kent (#476560R)	81	9
Kerstin	78	6
Kevin	58	9
Key To Cherished Teddies Town	169	8
Kim	92	2
Kimberly	98	7
King And Queen Of Hearts Collector Set	121	6
Kirby	115	6
Kiss Makes Everything Better, A	101	4
Kiss The Hurt And Make It Well	58	10
Kittie	59	1
Klaus	116	6
Kris	116	7
Kristen	59	2
Kurtis D. Claw	169	1
Kyle	59	3
Lacey	114	5
Lamppost Lights	115	7
Lance	59	4
Lanny (#CT005)	166	4
Lanny (#CT105)	166	5
Larry	59	5
Laura	59	6
Lauren	128	8
Lavender	160	2
Lavender Mitten	146	3
Lee	59	7
Leilani	78	7
Lela Nightingale	167	7
Leo	49	9
Letty	166	6
Lian	78	8

	Pg.	Pic.
Libby	59	8
Life Is Smooth Sailing With You	59	9
Lily (#202959)	84	9
Lily (#202959A)	85	1
Linda	59	10
Lindsey and Lyndon (#141178)	130	5
Lindsey and Lyndon (#141178A)	130	6
Lionel	115	8
Lisa	60	1
Little Bo Peep	109	7
Little Bo Peep (plate)	152	5
Little Bundle Of Joy (boy)	60	2
Little Bundle Of Joy (girl)	60	3
Little Jack Horner	110	1
Little Jack Horner (plate)	152	6
Little Miss Muffet	110	2
Little Miss Muffet (plate)	152	7
Live Well, Laugh Often, Love Much	148	12
Lloyd (#CT003)	168	7
Lloyd (#CT103)	168	6
Logan	93	7
Lois	100	8
Loretta	60	4
Lori	60	5
Lorna (#202452)	78	9
Lorna (#202452P)	78	10
Lorraine	92	3
Lotje	60	6
Lou	60	7
Love (#104140)	149	1
Love (#662089)	128	1
Love (#663794)	119	6
Love Blocks	106	2
Love Letters Display Blocks	106	3
Love Me	162	11
Luck	128	2
Lydia	60	8
Lynn (#310735)	60	9
Lynn (#310735A)	60	10
Machiko	79	1
Madeline	61	1
Mandy	61	2
March	88	3
March (plush)	161	4
Marco Pawllini, Bearector	165	10
Marcus	87	8
Margaret	61	3
Margy	61	4
Maria With Baby/Josh	108	4
Marian	121	7
Marie	61	5
Marilyn	61	6
Mark	107	1
Marlene & Marissa	61	7
Marty (#476722)	99	3
Marty (#476722R)	99	4
Mary	61	8
Mary Had A Little Lamb	152	8
Mary Jane	168	8
Mary, Mary, Quite Contrary	110	3
Matilda	61	9
Matt and Vicki	61	10
Matthew	97	5
Maureen	62	1
Maxine D'Face	164	6
May	107	2
May (Avon)	88	3
May (plush)	161	6
Mayor Wilson T. Beary	169	9
Megan	98	8
Melinda	92	4
Melissa	62	2
Meredith	62	3
Meri	117	9
Merry	89	6
Merry (plush)	157	13
Mexican Boy	144	10
Mexican Boy (plush)	159	12
Michael and Michelle	62	4
Mike	62	5
Miles	62	6
Millennium Event Bears	157	14
Millie	62	7
Milt And Garrett	62	8
Milton	62	9
Mimi, Darcie And Misty	62	10
Mindy	63	1
Mini Nativity With Creche	108	5
Mini Risers	103	6
Mini Tea Set	153	11
Miranda (#476706)	99	5
Miranda (#476706R)	99	6
Miss You	119	7
Miss You (plush)	162	12
Missy, Cookie & Riley	120	4
Mitch	130	7
Molly	63	2
Mom – Maker Of Miracles (plaque)	149	2
Mom – Maker Of Miracles (plate)	151	2
Mom And Boy Baking Cookies	150	2
Mom With Children	150	3
Mommy And Me	134	12
Monica	95	5
Mother	112	4
Mother Goose And Friends	63	3
Mother Goose And Friends (plate)	152	9
Mother's Day (plate, #156493)	151	4
Mother's Day (plate, #203025)	151	5
Mother's Day (plate, #476889)	151	3
Mother's Day (plush)	160	10
Mother's Day Mini Figurines, *Grandma*	63	4
Mother's Day Mini Figurines, *Mom*	63	5
Mother's Day Mini Figurines, *Nana*	63	6
Mouse King	110	6
Mrs. Claus Bear	118	1
Mrs. Cratchit	96	7
My Buddy And Me	135	1
My Cherished Family	135	2
My Cherished Friend	135	3
My Cherished Grandma	135	4
My Cherished Mom	135	5
My Cherished One (frame)	135	6
My Cherished One (plaque)	149	3
My Visit To Santa	135	7
Mystery Bear	164	7
Nadia	79	2
Nancy	63	7
Natalie	63	8

	Pg.	Pic.		Pg.	Pic.
Nathan	63	9	Paul Revere	65	8
Nathaniel And Nellie	63	10	Paula	65	9
Nativity	108	6	Pauline	65	10
Nativity Collector Set	108	7	Peach	160	4
Nativity Prayer	108	8	Penny, Chandler, Boots (#337579)	66	1
Nativity Pull Toy, Camel	108	9	Peter	66	2
Nativity Pull Toy, Cow	109	1	Phoebe (#617113)	66	3
Nativity Pull Toys	109	2	Phoebe (#914762)	107	5
Neighbearhood Accessories	113	2	Pink Mitten	146	4
Neil	165	11	Pinocchio	100	9
New Arrival	119	8	Playful	128	3
New Baby	119	9	Preston (#216739)	79	3
New Year's	160	11	Preston (#216739P)	79	4
Newton	64	1	Priscilla	66	4
Nick	115	9	Priscilla And Clara	66	5
Nickolas	116	8	Priscilla & Greta	66	6
Nicole	107	3	Priscilla Ann	66	7
Nikki	64	2	Prudence	66	8
Nils	64	3			
Nina	64	4	R. Harrison Hartford (#CT002)	169	3
Noel	102	5	R. Harrison Hartford (#CT102)	169	2
Nolan	102	6	Radio Flyer® / America's Promise®	162	7
Nora	89	7	Rajul	79	5
Norbit And Nyla	64	5	Ralph	66	9
Norm	64	6	Randy	66	10
Norma	64	7	Ray	166	7
Norman (#916692)	158	1	Rebecca	103	9
Norman (#916706)	158	2	Red Mitten	146	5
Norman (#916714)	158	3	Reindeer Carousel	140	4
Norman (#916730)	158	4	Rex	67	1
November	89	1	Rich	67	2
November (plush)	161	12	Richard With Camel	109	5
NSPCC Figure	64	8	Rick	129	4
Nutcracker Suite Collector Set	110	6	Ricky McBear	166	1
Nutcracker Suite Furniture Figurines	110	7	Rita	67	3
Nutcracker Suite Tree Musical	110	8	Robbie and Rachel	67	4
			Robert	67	5
October	88	10	Roberta	67	6
October (plush)	161	11	Robin	121	8
Oh Baby	153	3	Rock-A-Bye Baby	132	7
Old King Cole	152	10	Rodney	67	7
Older Daughter	112	5	Rodney (plush)	158	5
Older Son	112	6	Roger	126	5
Olga	64	9	Roly Poly Santa	158	6
Oliver & Olivia	64	10	Romeo	122	1
Once Upon A Time	132	5	Ron	67	8
Orchid	160	3	Ronnie	109	3
Ornamental Furniture Figurines	85	2	Rose	85	3
Oscar	107	4	Rose (plush)	160	5
Our Bundle Of Joy	135	8	Rosemarie and Ronald	67	9
Our Cherished Family	132	6	Roxie & Shelly	67	10
Our Cherished Family Collector Set	112	7	Roy	68	1
Our Cherished Wedding Collectors Set	114	1	Russian Girl	144	11
Our First Christmas	150	9	Russian Girl (plush)	159	13
Our Friendship Is An Adventure	81	2	Russell And Ross	92	5
Our Journey Has Just Begun	104	2	Ruth & Gene	68	2
			Ryan	68	3
Palmer And Charlene	65	1			
Pamela and Grayson	120	5	St. Jude Plush	158	7
Pat	65	2	St. Patrick's Day	160	12
Patience	65	3	Sally & Skip (#510955)	68	4
Patrice	65	4	Sam	68	5
Patrick	65	5	Sammy	109	4
Patty And Peggy	65	6	Sandra	95	6
Paul	65	7	Sandy	86	5

Alphabetical Index

	Pg.	Pic.
Sanford	116	9
Santa	117	1
Santa Bear	118	2
Santa Express Accessory Set	116	1
Santa With Hat	158	8
Santa With Toys	140	5
Santa With Tree And Toys	150	10
Santa's Workshop	118	3
Sara	68	6
Sara (plush)	158	9
Sarah	128	9
Sawyer And Friends	90	8
School Days	153	4
School Days Mini Figurines		
Boy In Baseball Hat	118	5
Boy With Book And Apple	118	6
Girl With Apple And Flag	118	7
Girl With Pom Poms	118	8
School Days Plaque	118	9
Scott	49	9
Scottish Girl	144	12
Scrooge And Marley Counting House	96	8
Sculpted Lapel Pin (#CT205)	166	9
Sculpted Lapel Pin (#CT305)	166	8
Sean	68	7
Season Of Joy, The	151	6
Season Of Magic, The	151	7
Season Of Peace, The	151	8
Season To Believe, The	151	9
Sedley	68	8
Segrid, Justaf & Ingmar	68	9
Sending You My Heart (#103608)	143	3
Sending You My Heart (#103616)	143	4
Sent With Love	68	10
Sentimental	128	4
September	88	9
September (plush)	161	10
Serenity	128	5
Seth	107	6
Seth and Sarabeth	69	1
Shannon	69	2
Sharon	120	6
Shelby	93	8
Sherlock	69	3
Shirley	111	5
Sidney	69	4
Sierra	69	5
Signage Plaque	149	4
Simone & Jhodi	69	6
Sister With Boots	143	5
Sister With Bow	143	6
Sister With Scarf	143	7
Sixteen Candles And Many More Wishes	69	7
Sky's The Limit, The	69	8
Skylar & Shana	69	9
Smile	162	13
Snow Bear	116	2
Snowbear	143	8
Snowman With Scarf	140	6
So Glad To Be Part Of Your Special Day	114	2
Soccer	163	4
Sonja	69	10
Sonny	70	1
Sophia	79	6
Spanish Boy	145	1
Spanky	115	1
Sparky	70	2
Spencer	130	8
Sports And Hobbies	153	5
Spring	153	6
Spring Bonnet Figurine (Blue)	70	3
Spring Bonnet Figurine (Peach)	70	4
Spring Bonnet Figurine (Teal)	70	5
Spring Brings A Season Of Beauty	152	1
Spring Mini Figurines		
Girl With Blue Bonnet And Duck	70	6
Girl With Daisy Headband	70	7
Girl With White Hat And Flower	70	8
Spring Sailor Plush	158	10
Stacie	70	9
Star	70	10
Star Plush	158	11
Stella	71	1
Stephanie And Melanie	71	2
Steven	71	3
Stormi	80	3
Strawberry Mini Figurines	97	6
Street Lamp And Bear	116	3
Sugar & Spice Mini Accessories	120	7
Sullivan	71	4
Summer	153	7
Summer Brings A Season Of Warmth	152	2
Summer Sundress Plush	158	12
Sunny	95	7
Susan	85	4
Suzanne	111	6
Sven and Liv	71	5
Swedish Girl	145	2
Sweet Flowers For The Bride	114	3
Sweet Little One	151	10
Sweet Little One Cross	149	5
Sweetheart Collector Set	122	1
Sylvia	71	6
T. James Bear (CT007)	165	1
T. James Bear (CT107)	164	8
Tabitha	71	7
Table With Food And Dog	129	5
Tammy	71	8
Tanna (#476595)	99	7
Tanna (#476595R)	99	8
Tanner	71	9
Tara	97	7
Tasha	71	10
Taylor	72	1
Tea Time	132	8
Teacher	160	13
Teaghan	72	2
Ted	130	9
Teddie With Toy Chest	140	7
Teddy	72	3
Teddy and Roosevelt	72	4
Terry (#686999)	72	5
Terry (#865095)	72	6
Tess And Friend	90	9
Thanksgiving	160	14
Thanksgiving Quilt	72	7
Theodore, Samantha and Tyler (#912883)	72	8
Theodore, Samantha and Tyler (#950505)	72	9

	Pg.	Pic.
Theadore, Samantha and Tyler (#950769)	72	10
Theadore, Samantha and Tyler (#951196)	73	1
Thelma (#156302)	97	8
Thelma (#789712)	95	8
Theresa	85	6
This Calls For A Celebration	73	2
Thomas	73	3
Three Bears Candleholder	132	2
Three Kings	109	5
Tia	95	9
Tim	49	9
Time Flies When You're Having Fun	132	9
Time Has Come For Wedding Bliss, The	114	4
Timothy	73	4
Tiny Ted-Bear	97	1
Todd And Friend	90	10
Tom, Tom The Piper's Son	110	4
Tony	116	4
Tonya	93	9
Too Much Work, Too Little Time	132	10
Tori	73	5
Town Tattler Night Light	169	4
Toy Car	116	5
Toy Soldier	143	9
Toys For Tots Plush	158	13
Tracie and Nicole	73	6
TravelBear Postcards	165	2
Trellis Display	121	6
Trevor	73	7
Trina	114	6
Troy	73	8
Trudy	73	9
Tucker & Travis	73	10
Two Bears Hugging	143	10
Two Boys With Lantern	140	8
Two Girls Hugging	100	1
Two Girls Standing	100	2
U Make My Heart Smile	101	5
U R My Favorite Friend	101	6
Ursula & Bernhard	89	8
Val (#738638)	74	1
Val (plush, #662291)	158	14
Val (plush, #662291L)	159	1
Valentine	161	1
Valentine Mini Figurines		
Hugs & Kisses	74	2
Love Ya	74	3
You're Purr-fect	74	4
Vanessa	85	7
Vernon And Eva	115	2
Veronica	74	5
Victoria	74	6
Victorian Jack In The Box	140	9
Victorian Romance	153	8
Violet	74	7
Virginia	87	9
Vivienne	166	10
Wade Weathersbee	167	8
Wally	93	10
Walter	166	11
Wanda	74	8
Wanda (plush)	159	2
Warren	126	6
Wayne	121	1
We Bear Thanks (plaque)	149	6
We Bear Thanks (plate)	151	11
We Bear Thanks Collector Set	129	6
Wedding (covered box)	140	11
Wedding (frame, #675806)	137	7
Wedding (frame, #675822)	137	8
Wedding Action Musical	140	10
Wedding Photo Frame	135	9
Wee Willie Winkie	152	11
Welcome	149	7
Wendall	74	9
Wendy	96	1
Wesley, Philip, Fiona And Renee	74	10
Whatever The Distance, A Friend Stays With You	75	1
When I Need A Hug, I Run To Dad	75	2
Whitney	75	3
Wilber With Teddy	109	5
Wilfred	85	8
William (#202878)	79	7
William (#202878P)	79	8
Willie	75	4
Willow	120	3
Winfield	75	5
Winnie	101	1
Winona	75	6
Winter	153	9
Winter Bear Gift Bag	159	3
Winter Boy	150	4
Winter Brings A Season Of Joy	152	3
Winter Church Building	113	3
Winter Outfit Plush	158	4
Winter Post Office Building	113	4
Winter Train Depot Building	113	5
Wishes	128	6
Wolfgang	117	2
Woody	82	1
Wyatt	75	7
Wylie	75	8
XOXO	159	5
You Did It	125	6
You Grow More Dear With Each Passing Year	75	9
You Have Taught Me What It Means To Be A Friend	91	2
You Have The Biggest Heart Of All	81	3
You're The Frosting On The Birthday Cake	75	10
You're The Key To My Heart Mini Figurines		
Key	76	1
Locket	76	2
Young Daughter	112	8
Young Son	112	9
Your Love Makes My Heart Smile	101	7
Yule	118	4
Zachary	76	3

Alphabetical Index